250 innovative ideas

250 innovative ideas

MADE IN BRUNEL™
Innovation that works

Made in Brunel
Brunel University, Uxbridge, UB8 3PH
+44 (0) 1895 267 776
www.madeinbrunel.com

Art direction by Chris Richmond

Editors: Ben Davey
          Eleanor Rogers
          Devraj Joshi
          Paul Turnock
          Clive Gee
          Stephen Green

Photography: Dave Branfield
             Patrick Quayle

Type set in Frutiger and Fedra Serif

First published in 2010 in collaboration with
Papadakis Publisher.

PAPADAKIS

An imprint of New Architecture Group Ltd
Head Office: Kimber Studio, Winterbourne
Newbury, Berkshire RG20 8AN
www.papadakis.net

ISBN: 978-1-906506-11-7

Butler Tanner & Dennis

This book is printed using 100% vegetable based inks on Respecta Silk FSC.
Respecta Silk FSC is produced from 100% Elemental Chlorine Free (EFC) pulp
that is fully recyclable. It has a Forest Stewardship Council (FSC) certification
and is produced by a mill which supports well managed forestry schemes.
The whole production process is managed on one site to further reduce the
impact on the environment

Kindly supported by:

Sponsored by:

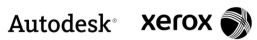

Foreword

Welcome to Made in Brunel: Innovation that works

Innovation is the key to success. Innovation is rarely easy and it certainly is not something that we are all born with, but when you have the sort of mind that can rise to its challenge then life is exciting, the world is full of challenges and everyone can see the significance of change. Innovation is the lifeblood of the world I live in, Formula One; it is the key to all progress, both here and in the wider world.

Made in Brunel is an innovation brand; it is a brand of young, creative and practical thinkers who have a zest for creativity and innovation. I am proud to introduce this extraordinary book, 250 Innovative Ideas, and the work of a remarkable team of young people from Brunel and their international partner universities.

I first experienced the unique spirit of Made in Brunel when it was in its first year: 2006. I met many students from Motorsport, Engineering and Design and was hugely impressed with their knowledge, their drive and their professionalism. These students were not just full of innovative ideas, they had the skills to develop, optimise and realise those ideas – these were future drivers of industrial innovation. 2006 was a special year for Brunel, their 40th anniversary and the 200th anniversary of Isambard Kingdom Brunel, an innovative thinker who transcended the boundaries of engineering and design. On a personal note, I was honoured that the University chose to award me an Honorary degree in this special year at a ceremony to celebrate motorsport engineering and design at London's Institution of Mechanical Engineers.

The Made in Brunel project has grown year on year, with over 700 young people now having taken part in this project. This year marks the fifth year of new ideas, fresh thinkers and industry-ready young professionals. Their ideas span all aspects of design, engineering, multimedia and, particularly in the production of this book, writing and publishing as well. This book is full of new ideas and an inspiration to everyone looking for new ways of solving problems. Made in Brunel is a student-led project which generates incredible excitement and I wish all the team who put this book together every success in their careers all over the world.

Enjoy the book, be inspired and believe that there is a world of innovation out there to be realised.

Dr Ross Brawn
Team Principal
MERCEDES GP PETRONAS Formula One Team

Contents

Innovation That Works

Welcome to 250 Innovative Ideas. The End.

That is what this book represents: the end. All good things must come to an end, or at least an ending of sorts. The end of successful endeavours, of sleepless nights and hectic days, the end. The end of an exhilarating journey. Moments past and failures dismissed. These pages represent the yield of a year's effort from a dedicated body of innovators and extraordinary creative thinkers; the very best that Brunel University's School of Engineering and Design has to offer, alongside the brightest sparks from other institutions worldwide that are Made in Brunel.

The project is now coming to the end of its fifth year and is – as it has always been – a showcase of graduate talent. We are once again returning to the Business Design Centre in central London to exhibit our work; we will also be making an appearance at New Designers and a number of venues throughout the London Design Festival. Now more than ever before, Made in Brunel is the Number One destination for consumers, producers and service providers searching for like minded individuals who understand that a synthesis of good design practice, comprehensive engineering and an innate empathy for user needs are the keys to unlocking the potential in their own organisations and the wider world.

With every passing year, we see the Made In Brunel family grow and grow. 2010 welcomes Tecnológico de Monterrey, Mexico, to the fray to stand alongside us with people and projects from Tsinghua University, China; the Indian Institute of Technology, Madras; Rhode Island School of Design, USA and Simon Fraser University, Canada. As the world becomes ever smaller it is increasingly important to build strong links with our international contemporaries. After all, we are better, connected.

The growth of the project is matched by its support from industry and for this we are eternally grateful. The HSBC Global Education Trust has been a source of continued espousal affording us the links required to develop our presence on the international stage. This year we have also enjoyed the support of Xerox and Autodesk as sponsors, with O2, West London Business and the Economic Challenge Investment Fund also offering invaluable support. Their status and influence in the world of engineering, multimedia and design, superbly complement the core values of Made in Brunel.

Based around an ethos of engineering excellence and compelling design as a means to solve real world problems, Made in Brunel rests upon the heritage of a prolific innovator and the forward looking institution that shares his name.

This year, Made in Brunel's emphasis is Innovation That Works. In a world filled with empty promises and exorbitant claims from faceless corporations about what we need and why we need it, we have built a philosophy based on openness, straight-forward communication and, most of all, practical and beautiful solution finding. Under the Innovation That Works banner, Made in Brunel has evolved into an open platform for networking and knowledge transfer. Over the course of the year we have been forging bonds with a number of organisations as well as reinforcing the existing ones with our industrial, commercial and academic partners.

For groups and individuals with the sheer passion for their art that those within Made in Brunel demonstrate, ideation is easy. This book however shows more than this, documenting developed and determinate innovations, many with commercial potential at the frontier of design thinking. The concepts and ideas in the book are divided into sections, which predominantly identify the arena in which they were developed. We hope that this makes it easier for you to find the innovators you are looking for, so you may grow your own networks and expand your horizons.

Every page in this book denotes a major milestone in the development of a project and its progenitors; moving out of academia into the commercial world. The quality of what you are about to see speaks volumes for their talent and dedication. For them, this book and the Made in Brunel platform is a springboard board out into the wider world and on to greater things. It is, really, the beginning, not the end.

Devraj Joshi

Director, Made in Brunel: Innovation That Works.

sustainable innovation

 Designs and strategies which aim to reduce environmental impact.

As we become increasingly aware of the impact of mankind on the planet, greater focus is being placed on the way in which we live our lives. Designers and engineers have a responsibility to create products that are both sustainable and encourage a more sustainable lifestyle. This movement has brought about a new, more responsible type of thinking that is socially and environmentally aware. Concepts within this chapter embody Sustainable Thinking.

Water Electricity Generator
Generating electricity using household water systems

With continual pressures from numerous arenas for people to act in an environmentally responsible manner, never before has it been so important to identify new sources of untapped alternative energy.

WEGenerator is an inline electrical generator capable of delivering useful energy from water in domestic plumbing without disrupting the flow. The generator has been designed to intergrate seamlessly with standard household pipes and can be installed using push-fit connectors or standard inline solder joints.

During use, the WEGenerator is capable of charging batteries, which may be used to power other devices, for example portable shower radios.

Kishan Mistry
Industrial Design BSc

Also on p.225

"People will not change their values, but design can be used to change their behaviour within their values."
Patrick Jordan

Approximately 60% of the UK's energy consumption is related to the heating and cooling of living environments. The thermostat is the interface between the user and the central heating system and therefore acts as an important facilitator in the bid to reduce energy consumption in our homes.

Conventionally, central heating thermostats have frustrated users, leading to poor understanding and incorrect mental models. This design aims to help the user heat their home in a unique and innovative manner.

Mitch Neofytou
Industrial Design BSc

Also on p.126

Wata Filta

Flexible rainwater harvesting system for tropical developing countries

The world's population is projected to increase by a further 40-50% over the next 50 years. This is of great concern due to the current water crisis ; more than one in six people lack access to safe drinking water. Rapid population growth, combined with urbanisation and industrialisation especially in B.R.I.C. countries, will increase water demand, ultimately causing great damage to the environment.

The aim of this project is to understand the needs of the immense underprivileged populations in the tropics in order to design an alternative, flexible, rainwater harvesting system for the supply of clean drinking water. The design is minimal and intuitive, light and portable. The active carbon technology allows for the absorption of organic impurities found in the mostly clean rainwater. The flexibility of this product allows for its use by a variety of different user groups such as outdoor sports enthusiasts and field researchers; however, due to its reliance upon rainfall, the product is most efficient in its target market of the Tropics.

Luiza Frederico
Industrial Design BSc

Also on p.165

New Composite Material
Converting MDF Scrap into Furniture Parts

This investigative project was a study into producing geometrically complex components and forms from the wood-scrap material and sawdust produced in workshops the world over. By altering the ratio of dust to resin, a wide variety of components with a range of properties can be produced.

In addition to making use of waste materials, the project gains additional sustainability merits by employing low energy processing techniques. New Composite Material is flexible enough to be used by small scale manufacturing outfits as well as artists producing single pieces of work.

Aleksandrs Malcevs
Industrial Design & Technology BA

Also on p.144

Water flask used to teach important water hygiene practices

Around 884 million people in the world do not have access to safe water. Worldwide, a child dies every twenty seconds due to diarrhea resulting from poor sanitation and other conditions related to unclean water.

Targeting water education at children allows knowledge and good practice to percolate through to homes, families and communities as well as establishing a firm foundation of healthy behaviour for future generations.

A personal water container for children in Ethiopia aged 5 -10 designed to aid education about water hygiene, and sanitation. Its form has been designed in a way that it is easy to carry around and contains the volume of the recommended daily water allowance of approximately 2 litres.

Also on p.52

Bola Adetujoye
Industrial Design & Technology BA

Tabeo

A roundabout mill for children in Ethiopia to grind

In many developing countries such as Ethiopia an educated workforce is in sparse supply. While education is held in high regard, it is often neglected in favour of serving more immediate short term needs. Time is a major factor in gaining an education, women and teenage girls in particular have to perform many time-consuming tasks throughout the day from collecting water to gathering firewood, all of which impinge on teaching time. Grinding teff, a small grain native to Ethiopia, is one of these tasks, which often falls to teenage girls.

Tabeo is a roundabout mill that follows a similar principle to a windmill or watermill - the children playing provides the kinetic energy required to turn the grinding mechanism. The project has a sustainable thread running throughout with the emphasis on assisting development in Ethiopia by creating a network of support to encourage entrepreneurs and provide relevant training.

Rebecca Doggett

Industrial Design & Technology BA

Also on p.134

Bath time is part of the daily routine for most children and, as such, it provides an excellent opportunity to help them become more environmentally savvy than their parents.

With the continued pressures on water supplies all over the globe, educating and influencing water usage behaviour is more important than it has ever been. Bathtime Toy introduces children to thinking sustainably about water through play and positive reinforcement. By submersing them in awareness of their water usage in a playful way Bathtime Toy seeks to build solid sustainable foundations and green habits amongst youngsters.

Also on p.238

Jonathan Aihun
Industrial Design & Technology BA

SolarGlo
Increasing solar energy awareness in Nigeria

Inconsistent electricity supply is a major concern for the citizens of Nigeria: electricity drops out without any notice and returns at unpredictable intervals, causing widespread disruption. Research has shown that one of the biggest domestic issues caused by this problem is the lack of lighting. When the electrical supply ceases during the night, families often use diesel-fuelled generators, which are expensive to run and produce harmful fumes. Poorer families tend to congregate together in one room and use candles or kerosene lamps, which can cause accidental burns.

SolarGlo is a solar powered light, with a wind-up hand crank, that provides a safe form of lighting for Nigerians. It has been produced to eradicate the use of open flames and provide more awareness of solar power in Nigeria. This will promote alternative, environmentally-friendly ways of generating electricity, rather than depending on the unreliable national grid, or using diesel powered generators that harm the environment.

Doreen Ojegba
Industrial Design BSc

Also on p.56

Globally the number of people affected by absolute or seasonal water shortages is projected to increase steeply owing to climate change and increasing demands. The UK is no exception to the rule with parts of the South East having less water available per person than the Sudan and Syria. Two key facts that can be used to understand the problem of water wastage and the potential implications if consumer behaviour toward water does not change.

Life is a product concept incorporating smart metering technology that compares household water usage to targets set by the national water board. If household water consumption exceeds the target levels, then the water supply to the plant is restricted and it withers. Living plants and real time feedback produce a strong and emotional analogy to the target objective. The concept aims to encourage people to consciously be aware of the water they use and the consequences that water wastage could lead to. As water sustains life on Earth, Life allows you to sustain a fellow living growth.

Also on p.131

Charles Cooke
Industrial Design & Technology BA

HydroGro
Bringing vegetable production to apartment living

HydroGro is an exciting new product for urban dwellers without gardens to practice small-scale agriculture at home in a mess-free manner by utilising a soil-free growing medium.

This innovative growing medium integrates hydroponic "water crystals" and aeroponic misting, plant nutrients, and water can be delivered cleanly and effectively in a precisely controlled manner.

HydroGro is efficient and a modern new interpretation of a fundamental industrial and otherwise hidden growing process

The transparent aesthetic of the HydroGro affords home gardening with a new, fresh, look as well as views of what normally goes on under the cover of top soil.

Thomas Kelham
Industrial Design BSc

Also on p.322

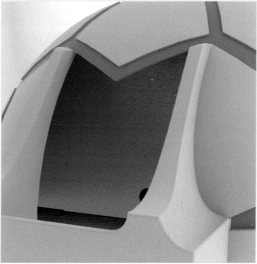

In recent years beekeeping has featured heavily in the press due to the proliferation of Colony Collapse Disorder (CCD), a problem first observed in the US during 2006, which quickly spread throughout Europe. CCD is a generalised term used to describe the recent phenomenon of thousands of bee colonies dying out without an underlying or recognisable cause. The economic contribution that all species of bees make to worldwide agriculture through insect pollination is estimated to be worth $90 billion annually. In the event that bees continue dying in such vast numbers, markets and agriculture will suffer inordinately, on an enormous scale.

Research clearly indicated that typical apiarists' equipment was not optimised for the typical apiarist; poorly designed and difficult to hold. This redesign of the smoker – a key piece of beekeeping equipment – focused on ergonomics, anthropometrics and other human factors relevant to the members of the target market.

Norah Lewis

Industrial Design & Technology BA

Also on p.136

EcoChair
Single use eco-seating for the events market

Ecochair is an innovative solution to the fundamental lack of seating available at outdoor events. The product is packaged in flat pack form for ease of transport and assembled by the user in-situ, using the simplicity of just 4 unique parts for a simplified construction.

Green credentials are at the heart of this project, the 100% recycled, 100% recyclable material used is fully FSA compliant, made with vegetable glues and printed with soya inks.

Ecochair is a ideal marketing tool, given by companies as a promotion. The low cost and large printable surfaces make the proposition to companies even more advantageous, with brand visibility possibilities endless.

Ecochair is compact, comfortable, light, cost effective and in demand, and holds enormous commerical potential.

Sponsored by EBP.ltd

Christopher Richmond
Industrial Design & Technology BA

EcoLyte
Engineered ultra efficient general lighting

Lighting represents 20% of total energy consumption in Europe. Studies have found that by utilising smart sensors and high efficiency LED lighting technologies considerable energy savings can be obtained.

This is more than just about energy conservation; it is cost efficient, service optimised and responsible. This is ethically important.

Utilising a total design approach a novel and well-engineered luminaire was designed to maximise the energy saving potential of LED.

This technology can help reduce energy bills and carbon footprint.

Thanh Tran
Product Design BSc

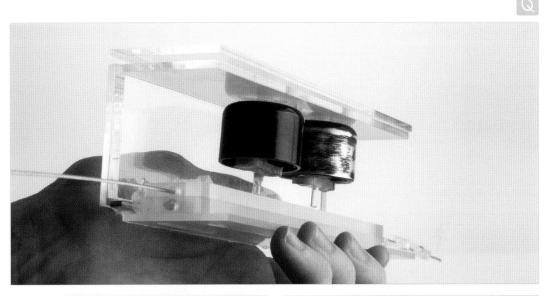

For people starting to ride bicycles and older people returning to cycling after many years, gears can be tricky to understand.

Lacking even a basic understanding of how bicycle gears operate, a cyclist is likely to have an underwhelming experience. Wrong gear choice can prompt cycling stalls, undermining confidence and potentially leading to injury. This project was undertaken in collaboration with a motivated and progressive team within Camden Council. Bel Gear helps cyclists by simplifying gear changes; allowing for a safer, more intuitive and enjoyable ride.

Also on p.139

Tom Wakeling
Product Design BSc

Esculo

Utilising food waste generated within the home

Food waste is a growing concern within the UK at a district and government level. Waste products can be treated as a resource from which renewable energy and useful agricultural materials can be generated. A national drive to expand the collection processes and technologies required to exploit this is well under way.

Current waste containment products fail to appeal to most consumers on functional and aesthetic levels. This presents barriers to more people engaging with their food waste and its management.

Esculo represents a concept that focuses on allowing users to easily engage, visualise and ultimately reduce the amount of unnecessary food waste they generate. Esculo has been developed to improve the implementation of existing technologies, whilst increasing the mass-market appeal through improved aesthetics and user interaction. The concept has been developed to be relevant to future waste management strategies and changes in user behaviour.

Tom Williams

Industrial Design BSc

Also on p.221

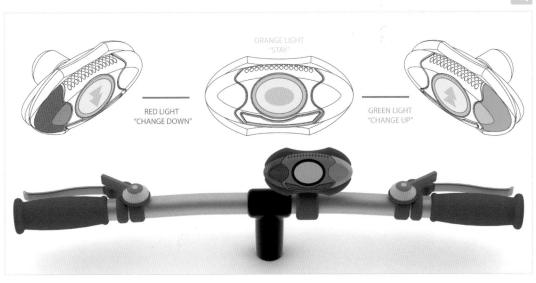

ORANGE LIGHT
"STAY"

RED LIGHT
"CHANGE DOWN"

GREEN LIGHT
"CHANGE UP"

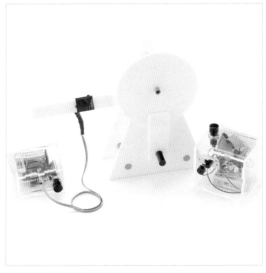

Easy Rider aims to alter cyclists' perception of gears to increase their pedalling efficiency. Effectively educating cyclists about gear ratios and their correct usage improves ride quality and reduces the risk of strenuous pressure on the knees and feet. By providing a simple way to understand gearing it encourages people to take up cycling by ensuring the entire experience is easy and controllable.

Easy Rider is an intelligent device which monitors and utilises real-time rider feedback as well as preset personal user data to advise the cyclist on optimal riding comfort and pace.

This product aims to bridge the gap between beginner perception and professional insight without adding complexity to the cycling experience. Easy Rider uses an interactive interface to actively engage cyclists regarding their technique in a universally understandable way.

Joe–Simon Wood
Industrial Design & Technology BA

Also on p.224

Semi Disposable Cycle Helmet

Semi disposable cycle helmet for London Cycle Hire scheme

The Semi Disposable Cycle Helmet was designed to provide a cheap, sustainable and convenient way of providing safety to people making use of the new London Cycle Hire Scheme. In a bid to ensure Camden Council's hire scheme is accessible by a wide range of demographics including the elderly, the Semi Disposable Cycle Helmet is lightweight and unimposing. By utilising a lattice of versatile cardboard, manufacturing, assembling and recycling the helmet is very easy in a socially and environmentally sustainable manner.

The design of the Semi Disposable Cycle Helmet underwent numerous revisions over the course of the project; each iteration affording improved comfort, fitting and impact resistance. The most current design is due to be tested against British Standards for helmet impact resistance and is expected to achieve an adherence rate of at least 75%.

Joe Snowdon
Industrial Design BSc

Also on p.241

MSc - Domestic Renewable Energy
Affordable solar energy for developing countries

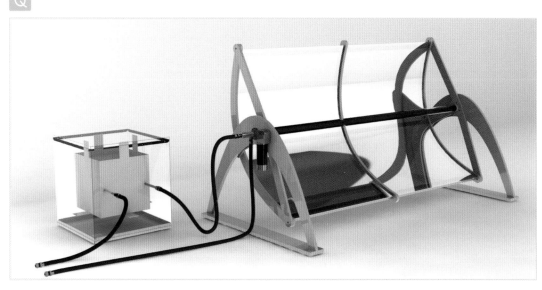

Affordable clean and abundant energy is key to prosperity. This is of particular importance for developing countries where reliance on existing fossil fuels and biomass lead to deforestation and smoke related illnesses. Energy costs take up a large percentage of income and time is wasted searching for fuel.

Luckily most developing countries are located in areas of high solar exposure. This project attempts to enable families to harvest this free and abundant energy through a simple and cost effective product, which is scalable to their specific needs. We found that in order to have a successful uptake of renewable energy we had to comply with two critical concepts: 1. Location independent energy usage 2. Time independent energy usage.

The system consists of three stages;

1. Energy harvesting: Implemented using a CSP (Concentrated Solar Power) system, more specifically a parabolic trough.

2. Energy storage: Implemented using rock filled heat storage containers.

3. Energy usage: Appliances which directly use thermal energy with heat exchangers.

This part is left to the local population to integrate to their specific situation and needs. This also has the benefit of a small industry to develop and bring new employment.

The product is designed to be a flat pack kit which uses local materials for parts of the system that make up the bulk of the weight. Particular care was given to selecting environmentally sensitive materials and processes, whilst trying to keep optimised system performance.

Loic Du Buck
MSc Integrated Product Design

The aim of harvesting energy from pedestrian traffic is a highly achievable goal, with both economic and ecological benefits in terms of its impacts and possible energy gains it could produce. The main harvesting technique is the use of floor covering on pathways and on stairs that convert the human's effort into electrical energy. There are several innovative companies pioneering this technology both in the UK and abroad but their primary focus is on the technology. London Underground are planning to introduce a trail energy harvesting staircase in one of the main stations in the city.

My focus is on the interaction between the pedestrian and these systems and the behaviour change required to make people want to to use them. A key element of this is the provision of easily understood dynamic feedback on the current and previous state of the system. To underpin and sustain the behaviour change of the user it is important to provide individual feedback. This will be done by providing users with individual RFID bracelets that will be read by the handrails on the system stairs. Users will be able to log into the system website and view the exact impact of their input on the system, thereby reinforcing behaviour change.

Colin Gallagher
MSc Integrated Product Design

Roof Gardens
Business communities and positive change

Q

A majority of my life and career has been in cities. I have been privileged to live in some of the most exciting cities in the world – Los Angeles, New York, Venice and now London. As my life and career have developed over the last 5 years I have begun to see that my "city lives" have been fast paced, full of opportunities, creative adventures and essentially self-obsessed.

In 2007 a colleague and I proposed a challenging and transformational project to the business I am working with - Wolff Olins. We proposed to take the 300 square foot roof top and transform it into a thriving vegetable garden to provide food for our canteen, experiment in urban food growing and to engage our people with doing something in response to climate change.

Wolff Olins is an international brand and innovation company and we are constantly challenging our clients and ourselves to create "better realities" in the world. Using design-thinking techniques, we invent beautiful pictures of what our world could be like - imagining new services, new business models and new expressions. At times we are able to implement these realities. Increasingly, I have become interested in not simply imagining - but experimenting with - possible futures. Not only for our clients, but closer to home - for ourselves. Individuals and businesses alike are being challenged with economic, environmental and social changes. I wanted to understand what we as a business community could do? What kinds of actions we could take in order to respond? How can we implement a positive, experimental and radical change – in our own way?

In 1973, Ivan Illich argued, "rather than maintaining a lifestyle which only allows to produce and consume – a style of life which is merely a way station on the road to the depletion and pollution of the environment – the future depends upon our choice of institutions which support a life of action" (Illich 1973: 57) Thirty-seven years ahead of his time, Illich foresaw a sustainable society as a working society, a society of encounter and interaction – not a society for consumption and the passive participation in entertainment.

It took us two years, many meetings, a few business cases, three drawings and finally we broke ground. We worked closely with a local charity that supports young people to work with businesses and create sustainable projects in Kings Cross. We designed two workshops to build and plant our garden. We worked with a willow weaver to create baskets, 15 students from all over London to plant the garden, and our lovely gardening facilitator to select and advise us on the plants and liaise with our kitchen staff and employees. We also built a wormery, composter and water butts to capture rainwater to be used in the garden. We now produce cauliflower, cabbage, tomatoes, spring onions, three kinds of potatoes, beetroot, raspberries, strawberries, rhubarb, spinach, chard, kale, lambs lettuce, a variety of herbs, fruit trees and more to come. We do not produce enough for the whole office, but we can see the loop we have created, we can observe the seasons and have a better understanding of our location and relationship to the environment then ever before.

In the midst of this adventure something else happened, we began to see the impact of being outside, getting our hands dirty, working with the community and gaining a better understanding of food. We have begun to grow a community not just food. Growing food became a design tool, a way of broadening our consciousness and questions around sustainability – questions that often seem far too big and difficult to fathom. This project has transformed the jobs of some of our employees, has inspired others to bring more of themselves to the office and has become a space to think and gather.

The exact ways in which this project has affected the business are hard to pinpoint and even harder to measure. We know that we now recycle all of our waste and most of it becomes compost for our garden. We know more about the varieties of food we are eating and how incredibly beautiful a cauliflower really is. We also have begun to see design as something much broader than a pretty package or image. This project was a collaborative, co-created design process. Creativity is at the heart of our methods and the project continues to inspire us to be more creative and develop more ideas for the garden. Success is in the doing and everything is hands-on. This project is one way in which we are beginning to redefine and explore design and positive change.

The garden is a continual surprise. We are increasingly excited by all of the fruits of our labour and the emergence of this project for our creativity, culture and purpose. It has helped us to connect with something deeper, to ask new questions and to connect to our senses not just our intellect. In poet David Whyte's book Crossing the Unknown Sea , he says "Maturity and energy in our work is not granted freely to human beings but must be adventured and discovered, cultivated and earned. It is the result of application, dedication, an indispensable sense of humour, and above all a never-ending courageous conversation with ourselves, those with whom we work, and those whom we serve..." (Whyte, 2001) Designing for positive change can be an instigator of collaboration, a tool for creating new realities and for re-connecting with work that is meaningful.

Happy gardening.

By Bethany Koby
Design Director, Wolff Olins

Bethany Koby is a designer, art director and artist creating brands, businesses and experiences to help imagine a positive and more collaborative future. She is currently based in London and divides her time as a Design Director at the international brand consultancy Wolff Olins as well as collaborating on participative models with art institutions, communities and businesses.

Bethany holds a BFA in communication design and a concentration in Art History from the Rhode Island School of Design. She has also just completed a Masters in Responsibility and Business Practice at Bath University.

Design for a One Planet Economy
One Planet Design

Q

Densely populated mature nations of the West are consuming the bulk of world's finite resources and energy. However, increasingly countries like China, India amongst others are growing massively and increasing the strain on these resources. If current trends continue, by 2050 humanity we will need a second planet in order to satisfy our demands for energy, commodities and water. Design for a One Planet Economy requires companies to align themselves to macroeconomic objectives and design their businesses to deliver an 80 percent cut by 2050 in climate changing emissions (CO_2) from direct and indirect sources. The UK government's move towards a 'One Planet Economy', as part of the new UK Sustainable Development Framework, emphasises that, 'a successful business is consonant with and operates within an economy that grows within the capacity of the planet's resources'.

Design for a One Planet Economy requires delivering new products and services with lower environmental impacts throughout the entire lifecycle. It also requires the delivery of innovative and competitive new business models and products with new design solutions. This program requires nothing short of major cultural and behavioural shifts-changes in our belief system. This, of course, is massively ambitious and has an evangelical tone. So be it.

A regulatory drive in reporting on carbon emissions will impact all companies across all sectors, not just direct emitters. Measuring the carbon footprint of a business provides a strong benchmark indicator across sectors, but is also instructive for setting goals within the innovation process. Analysing carbon will demonstrate that companies with stronger environmental strategies have overall higher quality management teams. Estimates have shown significant downstream potential liabilities if companies are required to offset their emissions. Certain sectors could literally face costs mounting into billions of Euros. Leading companies are setting carbon reduction programmes across all operations yet many are still far behind. For companies where most of the tonnes of carbon dioxide (tCO2e) emitted are from indirect sources there is an opportunity to reduce emissions through increasing energy efficiency and eco-design practices.

Giraffe's focus is on a design-led carbon reduction programme. All companies have a carbon footprint which is the emissions caused directly and indirectly by an organisation, individual, event, product or service. A majority of emissions come directly from heat and transport and indirectly from utilities, manufacturing and using products and services throughout the lifecycle. The process starts by establishing a baseline carbon figure. This accounts for the energy, water and waste associated with running the business. A number of approaches are taken to reducing this figure. The results from this analysis are factored into ongoing company planning and future projects within the live design cycle. The success of innovation projects is measured against their consonance with the company's year on year carbon reduction targets, along with the typical commercial objectives. Where reduction is not possible, Giraffe advises and manages companies on an appropriate offsetting mechanism. This is managed through Giraffe's One Planet Economy service (www.oneplaneteconomy.com).

Resource reduction is clearly the way forward. By this we mean that it is much better to reduce the amount of materials, energy and associated emissions required in the first place, rather than dealing with them at end of life, or mitigating any responsibility by offsetting. This is clearly the best strategy for the environment, for business and for the bottom line. Small changes can have a significant commercial and environmental benefits when aggregated across a business or entire sector. Recent carbon reduction projects by Giraffe have identified over £20 million in cost savings and over 50,000 tCO2e along with a number of potential new business opportunities. The benefits of considering embodied CO2 emissions associated with products and packaging are clear. One carbon-led redesign project undertaken by Giraffe looked at the company's packaging. The proposed redesign identified savings equivalent to offsetting the client's entire UK and Ireland retailing operations across 163 large stores.

This work leads to a significant change in processes and the culture of the businesses we work with, which results in specific pledges such as:

- Implementing an environmental management system
- Developing systems of internal reporting to help monitor environmental performance

- Embedding environmental concerns when developing and changing business activities, processes, products and services
- Engaging suppliers to implement environmental processes, policies and procedures in place
- Lifecycle assessment on innovation projects
- Setting annual CO_2 reduction targets across all business activities.

Innovation Techniques – Eco Dice™

Many scientists, policy makers and politicians, are, out of necessity, developing a better grasp of the environmental and ecological problems. Dr P.R. White of Procter & Gamble stated that "Sustainable innovation means finding new ways to do new things, as well as new ways to do old things." However, in order to achieve this we need innovation techniques that lead towards a new creative synthesis of innovation within the context of sustainability. The generic innovation process is well established. It can be seen as focussed converging activity. It underpins the activities of most professional subgroups. However, there seems to be something missing from the early parts of the innovation process. Where are the clear outcomes which are desirable, tangible and specific? Where are the visions and prototypes? We need clarity of perspectives and visions of a better future which are so clearly and convincingly rendered that everyone can make informed choices. There are new forces and demands being brought to bear upon that generic process. The green imperative means that this well established process continues but there are now new criteria, new activities and new tools placed alongside. In order to facilitate sustainable innovation we need experiential, visual, tactile design led techniques for exploring plausible ideas. Giraffe's Eco-Dice™ technique acknowledges the 'distributed' nature of innovation between 'actors' across the entire business, including external sources such as University research laboratories and users.

There is a tendency to stick to the same old solutions and to what you know – for the obvious reason that it is hard to stick to what you do not know. Creativity tools act as a catalyst for new combinations and connections. The Eco-Dice™ is a generative technique facilitated in workshop sessions and has been used to great effect internationally with innovation teams in companies across all sectors. The technique acknowledges two fundamental principles of creativity – constraints and randomness. Too often the environmental agenda is neglected within the innovation management process. This technique incorporates sustainability criteria with mainstream considerations such as cost, market, user, time and so on. The target is a proposal, an idea, a diagram, a programme, for a design for a sustainable business, product or service which matches the dice parameters. All ideas generated by the Eco-Dice technique are assessed according to their 'sustainability credentials' which include resources, energy, water, waste, social ethical and product service systems (PSS).

Companies of all sizes have a lot of power to influence change. We must not be victims of our own narrowness and knowledge. We have to take some form of structural understanding of ecology and sustainability. The way forward is not to make us all ersatz scientists, but to give companies a grounding in the basics of sustainability. This must be based on reasoned argument and sound science. We realise that from a business perspective, there is little point making environmentally sensitive products and services if they are not commercially viable. Yet there are commercial benefits in being ahead of the game. For example, the ethical stance a company takes inevitably contributes to its brand. For some it is key to differentiating their offering. For these companies making a profit and philanthropy are not mutually exclusive. For others it is about improving efficiency. New attitudes will pervade all strata of society. Businesses will operate according to new models. This is a simple choice because the alternative is that we slide, not with a bang but a whimper, into a morass of waste and toxicity. More than that, in the long term economic, ethical and environmental targets do coincide – because no company, no matter how adroit, can make money out of a poisoned population and a dead planet.

By Rob Holdway and David Walker

Giraffe Innovation Limited
www.giraffeinnovation.com

Giraffe was listed by The Guardian as one of the 10 brightest independent UK green businesses.

Ecological Enlightenment
The new phrase for designers

Q

A materialistic trait exists in every single one of us; for some, more primitively than others. Those engrossed in the pursuit of wealth run past this world with horse blinkers firmly attached, seldom looking to nature for a sense of belonging. Nature is merely a backdrop for human action and emotion, a canvas on which to paint. The landscapes of Constable remind us of our affection for nature, although ironically, they conceal a prosperous family corn business, tailoring nature into the common agricultural scene we see today. The Earth from a bird's eye view has for sometime now been a patchwork quilt of cultivation. Agriculture has ploughed our landscape into segments, pushing life into the hedgerows only for it to become imminent road kill. Worryingly, there is a more pressing issue evading the naked eye, one which we cannot manoeuvre around.

Take a look at yourself in the mirror for a moment and appreciate your organic reflection. You are an amalgamation of evolutionary complexity, the product of nature. Under your skin however, exists an increasing viscosity of poisons, delivered alongside your produce by irresponsible industrial producers. In a TEDTalk by, William McDonough, co-author of Cradle to Cradle, this failure is confronted whilst reading the label of an innocent looking rubber duck:

WARNING: This product contains chemicals known to the State of California to cause cancer and birth defects or other reproductive harm.

"This is a bird. What sort of culture would produce a product of this kind and then label it and sell it to children?" (TED, 2005).

The Industrial Revolution gave birth to this mismanagement of materials but still, its prevalence continues to threaten life today. Our reluctance to act upon these anthropogenic catastrophes is due to the reliance of embedded infrastructures. In no way do these infrastructures share our ability to improvise, instead the 'God's of Profit' are preferred. Mercury in the bay of Minamata, the meltdown at Chenobyl, even the recent oil spill in the Gulf of Mexico are reminders of how we place wealth before health. So as you recline in your cinema seat, watching Hollywood's 'mutant hero saving humanity', please remind yourself that in the future, the products of mankind should at least be kind to man.

Capitalism is the catalyst for this vicious circle of material consumption, but there is an awakening breaking on the horizon, an ecological enlightenment evangelically spreading throughout our communities.

Apple's recent love affair with aluminium emanates from an environmentally sensitive consciousness, fortunately strung with the chords of visual delight. Holding the new chassis that encases most of their products gives the beholder a sense of crafted quality. Like slabs of precious metal we hold these artefacts endearingly, protecting them from harm often Incase™ they begin to show signs of ageing. When the Apple starts to wrinkle, or worse rot from the inside, acceptance is a necessary part of our prescribed consumer lifestyle. It is doubtful the design team at Apple sat down to thank Mother Nature upon casting the monocoque chassis encasing the new 15" MacBook Pro, although their use of Earth's third most abundant material is at least reassuring.

Yet, this type of thinking, of being 'less bad', is not going to reconcile our unrequited relationship with nature. We are walking in increased numbers on ground which cannot be recovered and our exponential growth is creating new problems. But have no fear, for a new design solution is just around the cortex. Design for Survival (not to be confused with DFS), could be the new discipline in years to come. Imagine this design assignment:

Greenland is melting and set to raise global sea levels by 2 metres. Design a pair of hydrophobic boots that enable you to walk on water. You might need to think about desalinating sea water for drinking purposes.

Graduating from a university esteemed for engineering prowess, inspired by the forefather of an industrialised era, is somewhat ironic. The path laid before many designers is now drawn with green 'lead free' pencils and like Luddites we must break the chain of industrial inefficiencies and multiply like algae over ancient sea wrecks, consuming the bad teaching, whilst proliferating green wisdom. Telling this story to our childrens' children is also imperative for the prosperity of our ecology (and economy); it must be written in the chronicles of human history. We must therefore become narrators and activists, publicly showing disgrace in the face of bad design solutions. As a starting block, rather than treating the symptoms of our environmental degradation, might we ask if it is the right solution to the problem in the first place?

"I give you the new coal fired power station. Its chimneys have been retrofitted with a pipe network that is capable of capturing CO_2 that would otherwise warm our planet. Upon collection, we compress the CO_2 into a liquid vapour, transporting it to a site for sequestration. We then bury it and forget about our problems... and then we have supper, safe in the knowledge that less global warming is occurring."

Free market technological optimists are at fault for today's weak social cohesion. Their ingenuity in improving inadequacies and increasing efficiency is preferred over a solution grounded in social progress. They exist purely to sustain the embedded infrastructures on which the economy relies. They are incapable of change, of adapting to a new palette of materials fit for ecological consumption. Comfortably sitting on an oil reserve, the economy can thrive, using a material that has accumulated over millions of years. However, in developing countries where an increasing amount of fossil fuels are being discovered, technological breakthroughs are dehumanising societies that would otherwise strive together as a community. This absorption of technology into traditional cultures is catalysed through the medium of the 'global campfire', known to many as the TV. If cultural modernisation continues, the richness of humanity will begin to homogenize. The ancient cultures providing endless documentary interest will solely remain in the archives of the BBC.

If we are to reach a globally empathetic consensus, then green marketing needs to stop asphyxiating its market with purely environmental sales points. It should be broadened to encompass social, economic and political endeavours for without this rounded overview, we may fall into the chasm before the environment does. Just out of interest...Will these words remain in your memory? Or has the visual imagery throughout this book transfixed your materialistic gaze? Eyes glazed?

Please bear with me then, when I ask you to recall the advert depicting the George Foreman 'Lean Mean Fat Reducing Grilling Machine'. Eco-efficiency legislators listen up:

The answer to our environmental problems is not the 'Mean Green Carbon Footprint Reducing Machine', nor is it the 'Mean Green Human Footprint Reducing Machine'. A population cull is not the answer. The answer does not embody machinery because technology is not the long term answer. The answer lies within our understanding of each other, utilising humanity's greatest tool, empathy; for your neighbour, for your family and for your childrens' children. Otherwise down the line future generations may not enjoy the same standards of living as you once did. We would also appreciate not being 'green washed' for it creates a negative stigma that paves the way for the denial of climate change - life should not be about restrictions. An appreciation of all things 'human' and natural should be taught in schools, ingraining ecological empathy into our minds. Green thinking would then be the norm, a backbone of natural intellect. Economic agendas can still drive a nation's wealth however, but it must be for the benefit of the global community, not narrow localised interests. The idea of 'acting local' and thus 'thinking global' should be advocated. Obviously, many facets of society need to change; 'televison tripe' for example, promising pointless materialistic claims of happiness. The quicker we switch off from these illusions of prosperity, the sooner we might appreciate the more animated forms of life.

By Jon Walmsley
Industrial Designer

Green with envy:
Thou shalt not covet thy neighbour's Prius

Q

Spending our hard-earned money on "eco-friendly" products reduces carbon emissions and makes a political statement. But, are we really helping the environment, or just helping our self-image?

So you drive a Toyota Prius, have solar panels on your roof, and even use eco-friendly washing up liquid. You are setting the example for future generations. If everyone was like you… we would not be in this god-awful mess.

Or would we? It is our obsession with the usage phase that may be clouding our vision of the bigger picture… the total environmental impact. Our environmental issues are bigger than CO_2.

The great CO_2 debate has been raging relentlessly since the mid 1970's, and it has long been believed that we are the main cause of any increase in CO_2 levels in the atmosphere. In terms of CO_2 produced, all of the human industry, cars, and aeroplanes amounts to a total of 6.5 gigatonnes per year, which is dwarfed by the forces of nature around us. Animals and bacteria alone produce around 150 gigatonnes per year. Even with so many natural sources, CO_2 only accounts for 0.04% of the earth's atmosphere, defining it as a 'trace gas', so it seems surprising that the IPCC (Intergovernmental Panel on Climate Change) concluded it to be the "most important" greenhouse gas, especially when harmless water vapour has a much greater greenhouse effect than any other gas in the atmosphere, causing over 60% of the greenhouse effect.

Patrick Moore, the co-founder of Greenpeace stated that "the global warming movement really is a political activist movement", "I think it's legitimate for me to call them anti-human".

So how and why have environmental products become the main focus of reducing CO_2 emissions? In particular, the current obsession with CO_2 emissions, along with government and media 'greenwashing', is leading to a new wave of marketing, aiming products at the environmentally conscious masses.

In the car market, CO_2 figures must now be stated on all advertising, alongside fuel economy figures. However, the gCO_2/km only shows the emissions during the usage phase and so the consumer is led to believe this is the only important factor in an eco-

friendly product. In the case of the hybrid vehicle, consumers need to think about the entire life-cycle, from production to disposal of all of that technology, and consider the complications with recycling such a complex machine.

One particular report that has tried to dispel the myths associated with hybrid cars is the "Dust to Dust" automotive report, produced by Art Spinella, President of CNW Marketing Research. In this 458 page report, Spinella argues that only 10 percent of a car's environmental impact is in the usage phase, making a Toyota Prius hybrid less efficient than most 4x4s, due to the energy used during production and recycling.

However his life cycle analysis is based on a surprising number of vague estimations to produce figures in the strange units of dollars per mile.

The number of estimated variables leads to huge variation in the report's results, unfortunately giving possible bias to the outcomes. The report estimated that the average lifetime of a Hummer 4x4 is 379,000 miles, over three times that of a Toyota hybrid, showing clear bias towards proving hybrids to be some sort of elaborate marketing hoax, merely adding fuel to the fire of an epic argument between the environmentalists, and the sceptics. As American astrophysicist and author Carl Sagan said, "Extraordinary claims require extraordinary proof", and the CNW report is a textbook example of inadequate proof. The "non-technical" nature of the report somewhat undermines its credibility.

Although its methods remain unclear, the "Dust to Dust" report will nonetheless at least prompt people to question the information that they are being given and the intentions of the companies supplying that information. Of course, Toyota is only concerned with saving the environment if it helps car sales. The car business is a highly competitive sector and far from being a standard 5-door family hatchback, the Prius has, in a dramatic reversal, become an edgy political statement.

Perhaps the single Prius element that has come under the greatest scrutiny for its environmental credentials is the battery and the 1000 tonnes of nickel Toyota purchase each year to make them. The Nickel for the battery is mined solely in Sudbury, Ontario, in

Canada, at a plant that produces so much pollution that NASA have used the surrounding area to test moon rovers, as it is so barren and devoid of life.

So, perhaps hybrids will not help to save the environment as much as we are all led to believe, but they will undoubtably save you money on fuel costs and currently, in generous tax incentives. If you are thinking of buying a hybrid, just ensure it is for the right reasons. Lexus hybrids with a 4.5 litre V8 will do 0-60 in 5.9 seconds. And no congestion charge... now that really is green.

The hybrid car market is only the tip of the eco-marketing iceberg. Steven Kotler, writing for Psychology Today magazine, said "There are now 38 different types of eco-friendly toothpaste available at my local health food store and not one of them comes in biodegradable packaging". Surely this is an example of 38 separate companies jumping on the eco-bandwagon, while not truly understanding their environmental responsibilities at all. If these companies do not understand the simple concept of biodegradability and material life cycles, how can you be sure that the rest of the product is manufactured in an environmentally friendly way?

Steven Kotler continues: "Look, I'm the same as everybody else, I'm seriously glad that I can now buy an eco-friendly version of every product I use. But, whatever the design, these things still break. Or some better version is going to come along. Either way, the stuff turns into landfill in the end."

It is important to understand that every product, eco or otherwise, needs to be created and destroyed. In many modern products, the usage phase is far too short to justify the environmental impact elsewhere. The best way to make a truly green product, is to make a truly quality product. A product that can be broken, repaired, used for years, and then sold directly onto another user. Surely this is true sustainability and recycling. These are all characteristics shown by the world's most recycled product, the motorcar. If we were all to go out and buy a new Toyota Prius each, what would be the environmental implications of disposing of 700 million vehicles worldwide?

Forget carbon-offsetting, nickel battery powered, cars and high tech toothpaste. Become a vegetarian. Methane gas is 10,000 times more effective than carbon dioxide at producing a greenhouse effect, meaning that a single cow creates more greenhouse gas effect per year than your family car. But think about it... Our planet has had animals living on it for millions of years. Has anyone stopped to consider that flatulence is not a 'pollutant', and is perhaps just a natural part of the life-cycle of materials?

I believe that the designers of new products have a responsibility to understand the materials' life-cycle and maximise usage lifetime. With these two simple rules we can create quality products that last and put an end to our throwaway culture. Far from protecting the world we live in, our obsession with carbon is clouding our judgement of what makes a good product, and what makes us repair and maintain a product rather than just throwing it away.

So next time you throw away a broken or used product, think to yourself, should I just have bought a better one?

By Christoper Holloway
Industrial Designer

Power Care For Men
Future design concepts for The Body Shop

Currently the role of masculinity in society is under constant reinterpretation and scrutiny, with concepts such as the metrosexual man emerging and disappearing every day.

Among this turmoil, men are looking for ways to express their masculinity and yet still appear effortlessly handsome. This forms the basis of the "Body Shop Man" concept, allowing men to capture an appealing natural look. This facial skincare product range focuses on going back to basics, a strategy more

likely to appeal to the target demographic than more traditional cosmetic marketing techniques.

The product range uses an aesthetic which men would not be ashamed to have in their bathrooms or even bags. Whilst keeping in mind The Body Shop brand's simplicity, the forms take inspiration from product ranges with strongly masculine aesthetic themes and shadow the semantic of power tools.

Bola Adetujoye
Industrial Design & Technology BA

Also on p.25

The male Meditation Stool is a concept developed to extend The Body Shop's offerings in the male market whilst maintaining their strong sustainable ethos. With stresses of higher education and working life on the up in a chaotic and fast paced world; the well being of students is often neglected.

The significance of the negative effects of stress are often overlooked, especially by young men and meditation provides them with a tried and tested way of maintaining their well being. Like exercise, meditation releases a rush of endorphins into the brain, producing a sense of power and self-control. The Meditation Stool provides an effortless solution to introducing meditation and facilitating its practice.

Shuaib Ahmed
Industrial Design BSc

Body Shop Shaving Kit
Future concepts for The Body Shop

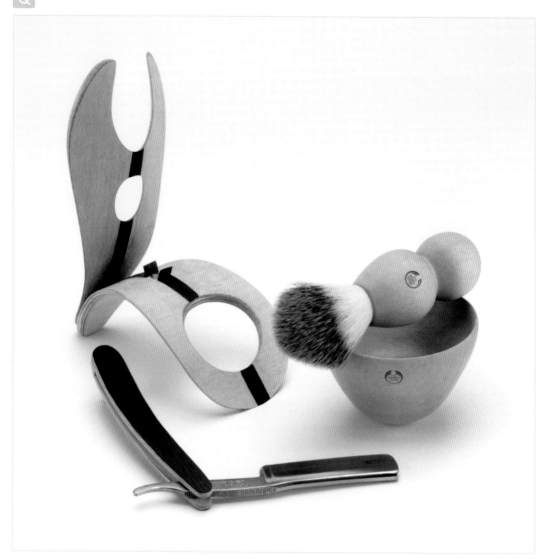

The Body Shop Shaving Kit has been designed to enhance grooming rituals for men, transforming them in to a holistic well-being experience.

The harmonic structure of the shaving kit cradles the separate tools in an intuitive and natural fashion. Wet shaving thus becomes a relaxing and pleasurable experience. The mixture of different woods and materials used in the construction of the kit imbues a sense of luxury and adventitious allure.

A product of this nature allows a man to take some time out to ensure his own well being and even perhaps pamper himself a little once a day without relinquishing his masculinity.

Anne Dah
Industrial Design & Technology BA

The Body Shop Reflexology Foot Massager for Men
Future concepts for The Body Shop

High levels of stress induced by the chaos and fast pace of modern life often have an overlooked negative effect on our well being and physical health.

The Body Shop reflexology foot massager aims to combat one of the many agitators of stress at its root. As the massager vibrates and warms the sole of the feet, key areas of the foot are stimulated to relieve stress in other parts of the body. This relaxation improves circulation and nutrient diffusion, increasing energy levels and happiness.

Doreen Ojegba
Industrial Design BSc

Also on p.28

The Body Shop is well known for their use of natural ingredients and sustainable philosophy.

Man Time aims to cater to the busy man who has very little time to take care of himself.

This concept aspires to restore the balance in lifestyle, improving personal well-being and reducing the stress that is accumulated throughout the working day. The Stress Watch is produced from sustainable materials. It monitors its wearer's heartbeat, temperature and voice level. If the watch registers a cumulative stress level which is too high, the watch face changes to indicate the level of stress and prompt the user to take 5 minutes to relax and have some 'Man Time'.

Michael Matey
Industrial Design BSc

Also on p.203

Future Concepts For Bridgestone

Kicks
Future design concepts for Bridgestone

In 2025, every child will want a pair of Kicks. By encompassing Bridgestone's values; "Trust, Journey, Safety and Excellence", these sustainable school shoes encourage children to safely complete the school commute on foot, reducing carbon footprints for them and their families.

Kicks are designed to grow with their owner over the course of their primary and secondary education. The leather features of the shoe are engineered to provide support and structure, allowing the expandable polymers of the central section to stretch as the wearer's feet grow.

In an attempt to combat the waste created by our disposable society and uphold Bridgestone's sustainable ethos, Kicks are designed to be upgradeable. As shoes grow and change with their owner, the soles can be removed, recycled and replaced. The internal features of the shoes provide support and good posture required as children grow.

Amy Godsell
Industrial Design BSc

Also on p.199

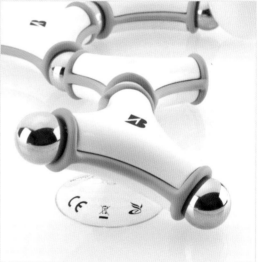

'Take a closer look at the great outdoors' Bridgestone's Caterpillar is a modular outdoor camera concept for children. The body parts, camera and sucker pads can be pieced together by a child, with the help of an adult, strengthening their generational bond. The flexible ball and socket joints and fully waterproof lens allow Caterpillar to be wrapped around branches, wedged into rock pools or simply stood on a windowsill. The fish eye lens captures images and video of animals and plants within close proximity. This is fed back to the child's computer, which interprets the images and then displays detailed information about the wonderful lives and interesting facts about the natural world.

Caterpillar not only helps bring generations together, but also gives children a greater awareness of their environment and the increasing threat of extinction in the world. When not in use, Caterpillar can be wrapped around the child's wrist, strapped to their backpack, or even hung round the neck for safekeeping.

Laura Hodge
Industrial Design & Technology BA

Also on p.74

Boris

Future design concepts for Bridgestone

Inspiring generations by bringing parent and child together to sustain energy with Bridgestone's environmental technologies.

Boris is a bath toy that generates energy and stores it during playtime. The movement of the propeller as the child has fun and plays, generates the energy, allowing Boris's cheeks to glow bright green at bedtime and protect the child from the nasty things which hide under the bed.

Bath time is a regular point in the day, when a parent and child spend precious time together. Designing a product for this occasion makes bath time a journey, builds trust, enhances safety and improves the whole shared experience.

Thomas Le Mesurier

Industrial Design & Technology BA

Also on p.101

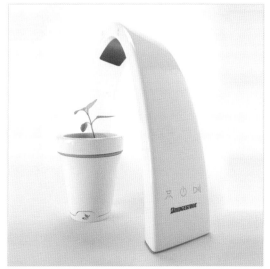

Arc was developed to enhance Bridgestone's position as a world leader in environmentally friendly and sustainable technology.

The body of the device houses all of the necessary equipment required to cultivate plants, herbs and spices from all over the world in a bid to reduce the resources used in processing and transporting food. In doing so Arc aims to bring families together through the shared experience of cultivation whilst teaching them about the environment and how to care for it.

Family members each grow a plant in their own pot. The pots interface with the main Arc unit providing an indication of how healthy the plants are, by lighting the pots and displaying icons above them on the main unit. Additionally, the hand held screen can provide information about the plants, their origins, biology and care requirements. Plant development is monitored by Arc which can provide suitable heat and UV exposure to grow even the most exotic species.

Chris Lynch
Industrial Design BSc

Also on p.103

Connec+
Future design concepts for Bridgestone

Connec+ aims to inspire generations by connecting family members through collective sustainable practice and positive environmental awarenesss. As part of Bridgestone's efforts to combat the effects of global warming Connec+ provides a system which can capture the energy generated by everyday movement and use it to power mobile items around the home.

By tracking the progress and performance of users linked to the base unit, Connec+ encourages a little friendly competition amongst family members, imbuing a sense of achievement and excellence. Connecting each family member wirelessly opens up networks and incentives for them to be the most sustainable within their clan as well as educating them about the importance of energy usage.

Nick Pettett
Industrial Design & Technology BA

Also on p.197

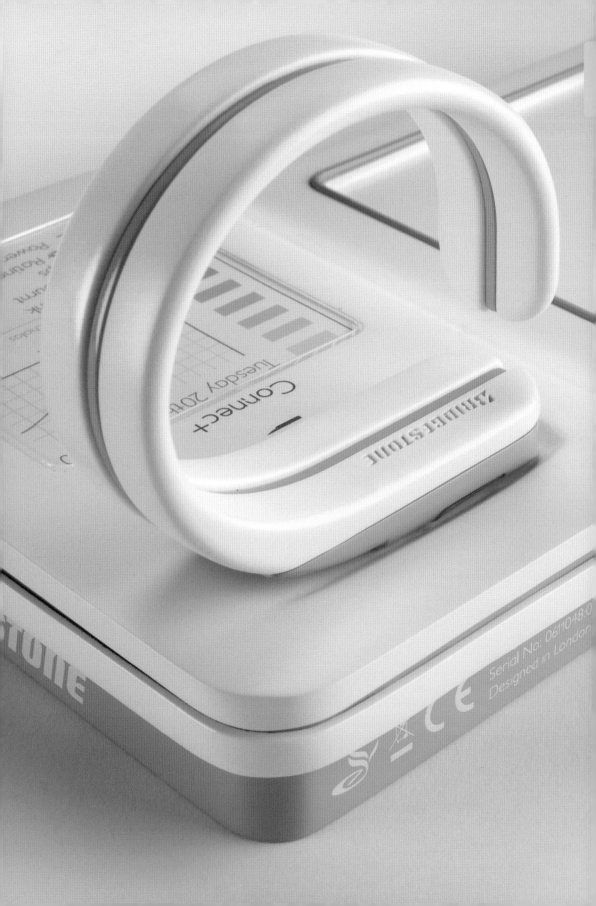

technical innovation

Innovative use of manufacturing, materials and electronics

Technologies are continually developing, creating new and innovative possibilities. Technical thinking embodies reapplying existing technologies to new situations to create innovative design solutions. It is this type of thinking that pushes boundaries and questions what can be done, resulting in great advances that shape the future.

AlarmLock
Innovative bicycle theft prevention device

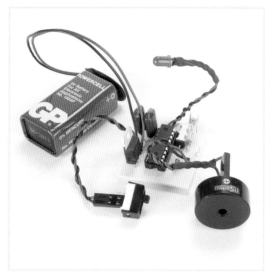

As people become more and more aware of their effects on the environment, an increasing percentage of commuters are choosing to travel by bicycle, eschewing other less sustainable forms of transport.

With the rate of bicycle theft already high up the rankings in the British National Crime Recording Standard, this new influx of cyclists only serves to widen the breach of targets for thieves. In 2008 a bicycle was stolen every five minutes and the problem is not unique to the UK; the prevalence of the problem

in China is larger by an order of magnitude.

AlarmLock is a unique and inclusive bicycle protection device tailored for the Chinese market. Once installed, the device immobilises the rear wheel of the bicycle and sets off a piercing alarm in the event of a threat being detected.

Luke Wilson
Industrial Design BSc

Also on p.317

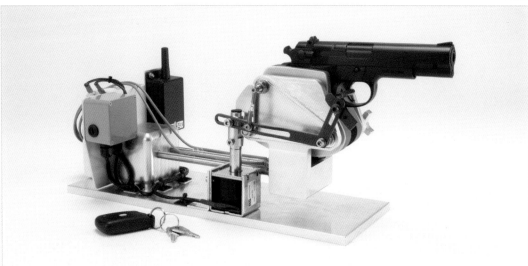

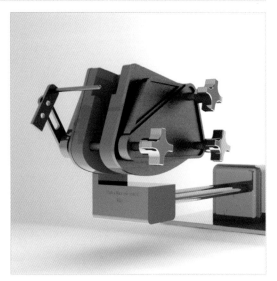

The Home Office Scientific Development Branch is embarking on plans to assess 9mm ammunition for UK police forces. This test rig was developed in order to allow for the execution of fair and comprehensive ammunitions testing.

By automating the testing process, the test rig mitigates errors introduced by human intervention in the test protocol and minimises the number of other time independent variables. This in turn affords consistent and accurate measurements of

weapon recoil during use. This will refine the process considerably and optimise consistency.

In no way does this project promote the use of firearms and the device should only be operated by trained firearms officers; its continued use at the Home Office should improve gun safety for all law enforcement officers.

Sanjeev Lal
Mechanical Engineering with Automotive Design BEng

In Touch
Bridging the communication gap between scuba diver and dive boat

"It is a scuba diver's nightmare: surfacing to find yourself alone with your boat nowhere in sight"

Drowning is listed as the largest cause of fatalities amongst scuba divers. General fatigue has been highlighted as one of the primary causes of drowning and so it is essential that stranded divers do not over exert themselves whilst awaiting rescue.

Communication between diver and boat is impossible once the two are separated by water and so there is no way for either party to keep track of the other's location; a new communication product is needed.

In Touch makes use of cutting edge electromagnetic and GPS technologies to facilitate communication between boat and diver. By making use of well established diving hand signals, In Touch is easy for divers to use intuitively. Signals are transmitted to the surface, keeping an continuous open channel of communication between diver and boat ensuring the experience is safe and enjoyable.

Samantha Mire
Product Design BSc

Also on p.112

DrinkSafe
Drink spiking prevention device

The spiking of drinks to facilitate criminal activity such as robbery and sexual assault is a high profile issue in the UK hospitality scene. With the majority of victims in the 18 to 25 demographic, a particularly vulnerable social group, DrinkSafe was focused on finding an unobtrusive method of protecting them.

DrinkSafe protects beverages from contamination by other fluids and powders. By using an infrared enabled fob or ring, the drinker may unlock their DrinkSafe in order to quaff. The interface has been designed to be intuitive enough to operate in a dark environment by possibly inebriated individuals whilst remaining impenetrable enough to deter those with malicious intent.

Peter Abel
Industrial Design & Technology BA

Munio

An intelligent laptop security solution for travellers

Laptop theft has been on the increase since 2009 and as the "return on investment" for thieves increases with each new technology revision, so does the damage sustained by individuals and companies both in terms of material and data loss.

Munio monitors the laptop and its bag and activates an alarm if any movement is detected; prompting the owner to check their belongings. In the event that the laptop has been removed, the owner may trigger a secondary alarm, which is attached to the laptop. This remote action attracts attention to the thief, prompting them to panic and drop the stolen goods.

Daniel Beavis
Product Design BSc

Also on p.106

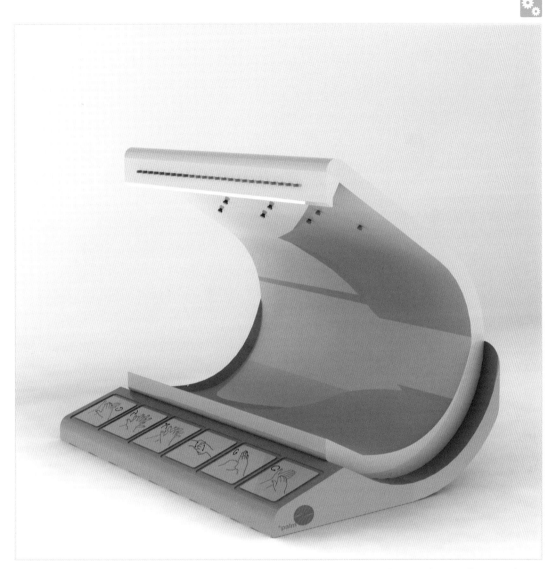

Ensuring that hands are correctly cleaned is the cheapest and most effective way of preventing the spread of disease. Studies indicate that there are between 600,000 and 1 million cases of gastrointestinal illnesses recorded each year in the UK, the majority of which could be avoided by simply practising better hand hygiene techniques.

The Palm One provides an innovative solution to guarantee better results compared to the common alternative, as well as educating the user on the widely recommended procedures for complete hand sanitation. In an environment that has seen little real development over recent years, this product stands out as a unique answer that will encourage the user to take notice.

Also on p.154

Nathan Brown
Industrial Design & Technology BA

Amulet
Providing a sustainable solution to hand sanitation

Despite over 80% of all diseases transmitted via human contact, less than 30% of the population wash their hands after coughing or sneezing. Hand sanitation should be part of the everyday routine for all of us but instead only really comes to the fore as fall out from media hype about the currently proliferating pandemic.

This project set out to find a method of personal hand sanitation more sustainable than alcohol gels. Targeted at city commuters, Amulet's form was designed to be compact, feel desirable, encourage people to touch it and run it through their hands. The cast aluminium and sculpted features gently diffuse a sense of luxury. Amulet is a refillable spray sanitizer providing feedback to the user using a thermochromic interface.

Laura Hodge
Industrial Design & Technology BA

Also on p.61

Patient exposure to pathogenic microorganisms during hospital stays contributes significantly to both the tangible and intangible costs of Health Care Associated Infections. Correct hand hygiene techniques applied by health care workers have been identified as a key measure of prevention. However, poor accessibility and underestimations in their affectivity are significant barriers to motivation.

Motionflow is a hand activated sanitizer dispenser, which aims to encourage health care worker compliance rates. Research into psychological and emotional factors, in addition to hospital layouts and architecture creates a user-focused product that enhances the experience, whilst increasing patient trust.

Sharan Kaur
Industrial Design & Technology BA

Also on p.244

Over the last 15 years, every aspect of the mountain bike has changed to meet the demands of the sport's toughest challenge; downhill racing. The gear system is the only component that has not changed fundamentally over the last century.

The 'LINK' gear system is designed to change gears in an innovative way never before seen in the mountain biking arena. LINK operates around an expanding chain ring that affords multiple gear ratios, and seamless shifting, while maintaining the perfect chain-line to the rear wheel for maximum efficiency.

Furthermore, by employing the centralisation of mass principle, the bike's suspension action is improved. This gives superior rider control in rough terrain, increased cornering ability, better weight distribution and balance in the air, allowing World Cup racers to ride faster, and push harder, than ever before.

Also on p.162

Chris Holloway
Industrial Design BSc

Flora Pudica
Solving the problem of dirty brushes

Many hairbrushes are discarded far too early in their life cycle due their dirtiness, rather then being broken or damaged. Flora Pudica is a new range of hairbrushes that eliminates the pain and hassle involved in attempting to extricate locks of hair trapped amongst brush bristles.

The mechanism designed in to the body of the brush dramatically reduces cleaning time encouraging the user to keep the brush clean. By removing the stray detritus from the brush it is no longer a breeding ground for bacteria and other pathogens. Flora Pudica has been well developed in the context for design for manufacture and assembly with reference to its form and mechanism.

Terence J Lee
Industrial Design BSc

Also on p.233

Single cylinder engines have historically suffered very badly from vibrations produced by the unbalanced shaking forces generated by the reciprocating motion of the piston assembly and the rotation of the crankshaft assembly. These shaking forces can be so severe that they can reduce component life, increase the loads imparted onto various components and at worst cause the motorcycle as a whole to be a thoroughly unpleasant form of transport.

By the use of a suitable method of balancing the aim of this project is to discover whether it is possible to design a single cylinder internal combustion engine that produces no shaking forces or turning moments due to the motion of the moving components.

Theo Rutter
Mechanical Engineering MEng

Onboard Tyre Telemetry
An automated solution to tyre quality control

Tyres are a vital component in any vehicle, playing a major role in its safety and performance. Despite each tyre only having a human footprint's worth of contact area with the road surface at any one time, they affect grip, acceleration, steering, braking and cornering. Despite this, tyres are the most commonly overlooked area of vehicular maintenance.

The Onboard Tyre Telemetry system automatically analyses fitted tyres at regular intervals, determining whether they are in an acceptable and legal condition. The Onboard control unit informs the individual responsible for the vehicle as to the appropriate action required for continued safe motoring.

Michael Evans
Product Design BSc

Also on p.109

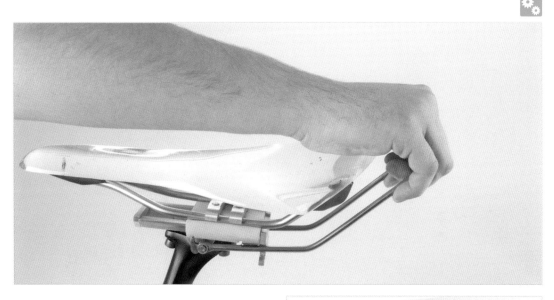

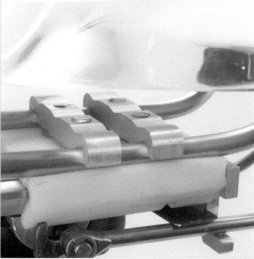

As the link between cycling and erectile dysfunction gains awareness, the lack of any method to improve men's health becomes ever the more glaring. The 120,000+ competitive triathletes registered in the UK alone, only serve to further exacerbate the flagrance of the omission.

ICIT 'Move' is an adjustable retrofit saddle designed to reduce pressure on sensitive areas of the male anatomy. The mechanism was designed to provide adjustment levels suitable for high performance athletes during competitive events. The saddle support structure and adjustment mechanism are manufactured from lightweight composites to ensure comprehensive structural integrity and efficiency at the lowest weight.

Rob Musselbrook

Also on p.323

Industrial Design & Technology BA

Electronic Telltale

A pressure sensitive tool for tuning a dinghy sail

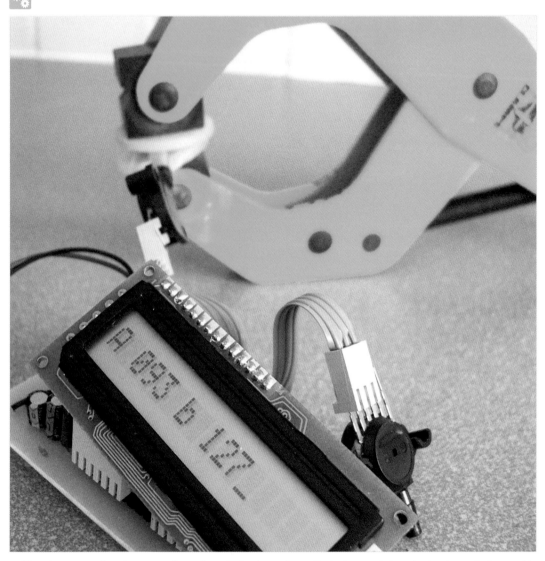

Sailing is a sport that is easy to learn but difficult to master. One of the key activities in sailing is the setting of the main sail; the primary source of power for the boat. Teaching helmsmen how to optimise their dinghy sails is a finely nuanced task, which this product aims to assist with. Using sensors attached to the sail, the Telltale is able to inform the helmsman about the forces being generated by the sail and visually indicate how to tweak the sail to make better use of the available wind power.

The Telltale is a training device intended to guide helmsmen, gradually honing their ability and instincts though the use of visual feedback and the provision of detailed information.

Matthew Perry

Product Design BSc

Also on p.113

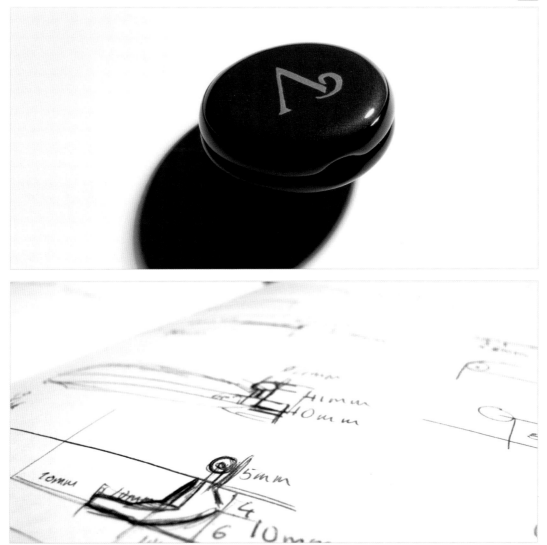

Per Sempre ("for keeps") is a transitional redesign of a ladies' powder compact; bridging the gap between new age and traditional make up accessory design.

Targeted in to the luxury market segment, Per Sempre retains all of the glamour associated with traditional compacts while affording the owner enough room to inject a little of their own personality. In order to enhance the compact's user experience, measures were taken during the design process to ensure that Per Sempre was durable, easy to use, resistant to impact and easy to refill. The combination of these facets should help to dispel the stigma current associated with getting a compact out in a public place and hopefully alter public perception of compacts towards something that is for keeps, rather then a disposable item.

Louisa Santilli
Industrial Design & Technology BA

Also on p.149

SWL Sensor

A system to improve the treatment of kidney stones using lithotripsy

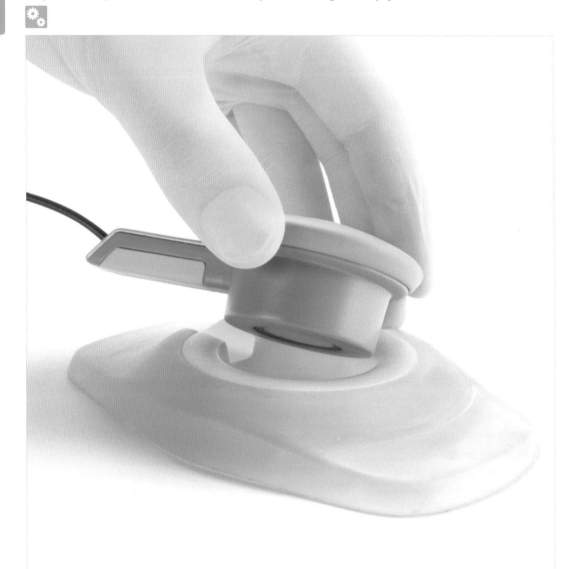

Shockwave lithotripsy, (SWL) is the preferred modality for the treatment of renal and ureteric stone disease. At present, the methods of monitoring the effectiveness of the treatment are insufficient.

This product aims to provide information during SWL that will improve the diagnostic capabilities of lithotripter operators and clinicians, helping unskilled practitioners achieve greater results during specialised treatment.

In collaboration with Guy's & St Thomas' Charity trust, this project builds upon long running R&D that was proven in the clinic but unusable in the hands of its intended operator. Making the apparatus easier to use and information more suitably comprehensive and targeted created a design solution created that aids Guy's & St Thomas' in moving forwards towards their goal of commercialisation. This device will reduce tissue damage during treatment, cut waiting times for the procedure by up to one third, and lower the number of patients needing re-treatments.

Chris Place

Industrial Design & Technology BA

Also on p.128

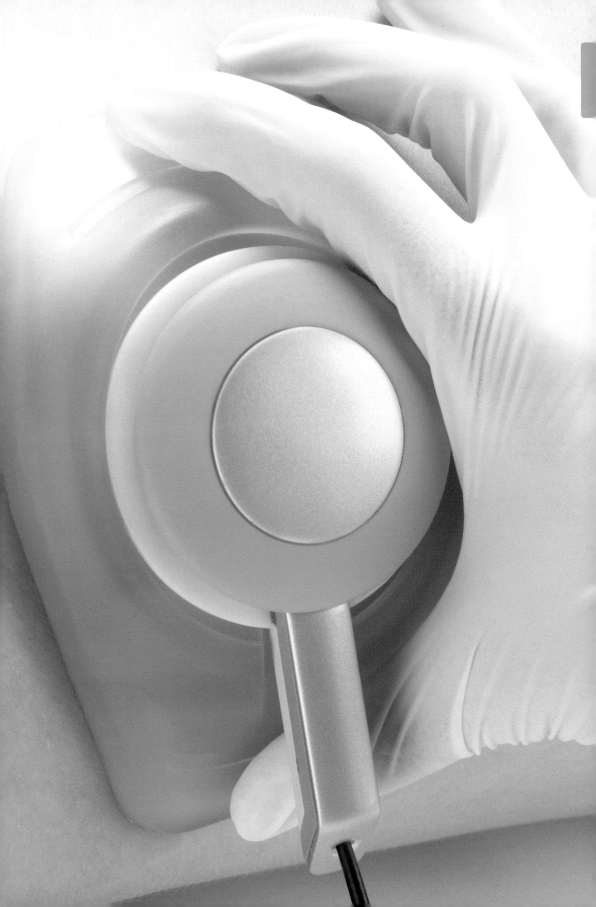

Fitting Room 'Smart Scan'

Eliminating theft within the fitting room

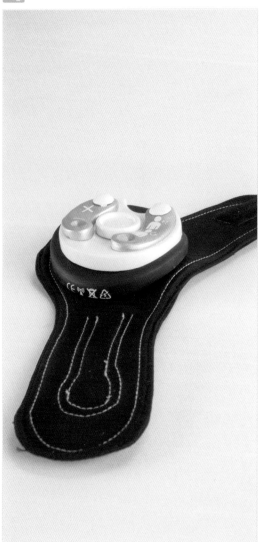

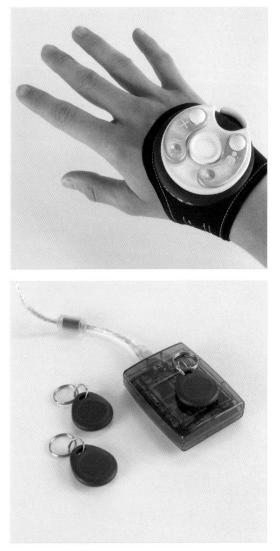

Shoplifting is an issue especially prolific in the fashion sector due to the presence of fitting rooms in clothes stores. Privacy legislation prohibiting any monitoring in fitting rooms makes them an ideal environment for theft to take place – offering thieves the time and seclusion they require to shoplift.

As such, the only feasible method of combating fitting room thefts is to carefully monitor the movement of goods at the entry and exit points of the fitting room area. Smart Scan is a hand mounted device which

allows staff to monitor items entering and leaving a fitting room in real time, visualising the inventory on a separate screen.

The operational design of the device has been optimised to ensure staff alertness and minimise the chances of human error, both fundamental causes for shoplifters escaping without reprimand.

Daniel Trigg

Industrial Design BSc

Also on p.316

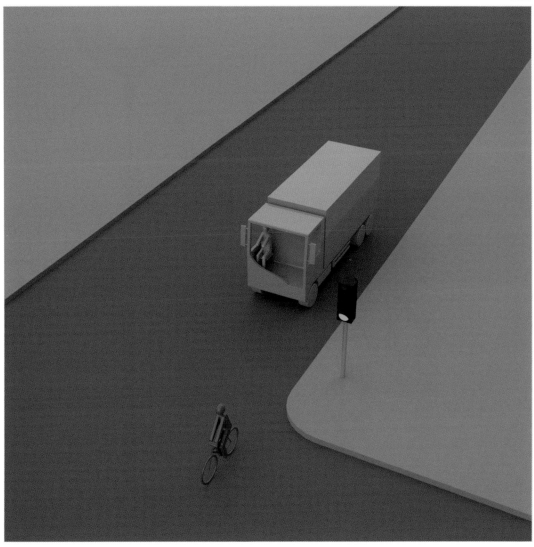

Heavy Goods Vehicles (HGVs) account for 4% of London's traffic flow and they are responsible for the largest proportion of pedal cyclist fatalities in the city. If a cyclist rides in close proximity to a HGV, entering the blind spot, there is a distinct possibility of the driver being unaware of their road presence whilst manoeuvring towards them, causing a life threatening collision.

To aid a driver's poor situational awareness, an intuitive vibration in the seat provides feedback as to the whereabouts and close proximity of a cyclist. By exploiting the inherent advantages of haptic feedback, the problems of visual overload can be mitigated, leading to a reduced mental effort and a quicker reaction time. The product is designed to be fully retrofitable to existing driver interfaces due to the difficulty of replacing HGV seats.

Also on p.127

Jon Walmsley
Industrial Design BSc

Brollii
Rain protection system

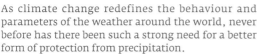

As climate change redefines the behaviour and parameters of the weather around the world, never before has there been such a strong need for a better form of protection from precipitation.

Brollii has been designed to withstand the demanding conditions, which our current climate pervades. While traditional umbrellas deform permanently into a safety hazard, Brollii's flexible ribs allow the entire canopy to flex when subjected to gusts of wind, reducing the risk of inversion and damage.

Additionally, Brollii also combats problems associated with storing wet umbrellas by allowing the canopy and ribs to fully retract back into the main body. Brollii is a fresh, innovative and stylish product that questions the long-standing current designs.

Simon Warne
Industrial Design & Technology BA

Also on p.135

This product aims to reduce Health Care Acquired Infections by ensuring the use of alcohol gel at the entrance to hospital wards. The final design specifies a system by which forced compliance of hand gel use is imposed at the entrance to wards. The system incorporates a gel dispenser integrated with the door lock. The lock is only released when the dispenser is used. The innovative design means that visitors who are unaware of the issues with hand hygiene do not pose a threat to patients. The design incorporates two posters. One to be placed on the door, with clear instructions to use the dispenser, and the other adjacent to the dispenser demonstrating its use. The second poster will also include instructions for the override button, which should be used by persons who for valid reasons are unable to use gel. Human factors have also been considered to ensure that not only is the design of the dispenser inclusive, but also that its shape encourages correct use, and minimises the chance of wasted or inadequate gel application.

Elizabeth Wolseley-Hext
Product Design Engineering BSc

Antimicrobial Pen

Reducing infections on writing equipment

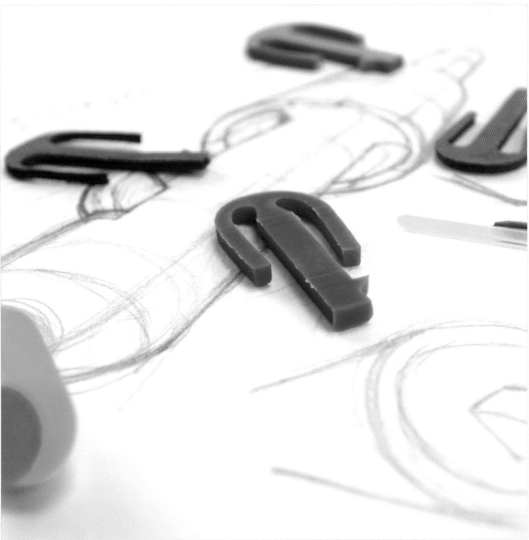

Healthcare Acquired Infections (HCAI) are a problem within hospitals and care homes alike, having been prevalent in England for the last twenty five years, infecting patients, staff and visitors. These infections are predominately spread through surface contact, in particular hands. Equipment and surfaces therefore require constant cleaning.

Where products are in continual contact with Healthcare workers' hands, additional precautions must be taken to optimise hygiene.

Writing equipment is consistently carried around by members of staff, placed in mouths and dropped on the floor without ever being cleaned and this clearly raises serious issues about their appropriateness in Healthcare environments. 71% of pens were contaminated with a common infection strain, with other strains present too.

The Antimicrobial Pen removes or reduces these issues while meeting the needs of Healthcare workers, decreasing the build-up of organic material.

Russell Anley
Industrial Design & Technology BA

Also on p.151

The SMART motorcycle helmet was developed to improve the survivability of motorcycle accident victims by providing attending paramedics and other medical personnel with vital medical information. Having instant access to medical data of this nature allows physicians to make informed treatment decisions quickly and effectively.

A combination of printed media and radio frequency identification technology allows data related to the wearer to be stored in a robust manner which can then be read without removing the helmet.

David Baker
Product Design BSc

Motorcycle Luggage Solution

Intelligent pannier design for biker usability

With an increasing number of motorcyclists today engaging in commuting, adventure and touring holidays riders are demanding more sophisticated and versatile luggage management solutions.

With an emphasis on 'biker usability' this innovative pannier was designed to provide the rider with an easy to access storage system which helps to prevent spillages. The elevated postioning of the pannier ensures that finding and retrieving items stored inside it is comfortable and efficient.

By allowing a pair of panniers to lock together into a single, stable unit with pull along wheels and a retractable handle, this design dramatically improves upon off-bike portability and ergonomics in comparison to existing products.

In addition to improving user experience, this project has had a strong focus on design for manufacture, ultimately producing a fully resolved design solution ready for production.

Ben Davey
Industrial Design BSc

Also on p.222

Agility and reaction time are important to many athletes. The interactive training device was designed to assist team sports coaches implement agility-focused training philosophies currently being adopted by a number of sports organisations including the FA. The final design will take the form of a cone.

Training cones come in sets of five, consisting of four positional markers and a master. Placing the positional markers in a square with the master cone in the centre allows coaches to run a number of different training exercises including movement patterns, ball control and passing/team play. The cones monitor and log time, distance, accuracy and other performance variables allowing those training to monitor their progress and set targets.

Oliver Diebel
Product Design Engineering BSc

Snowsport Performance H.U.D

A display which loses the need for handheld performance products

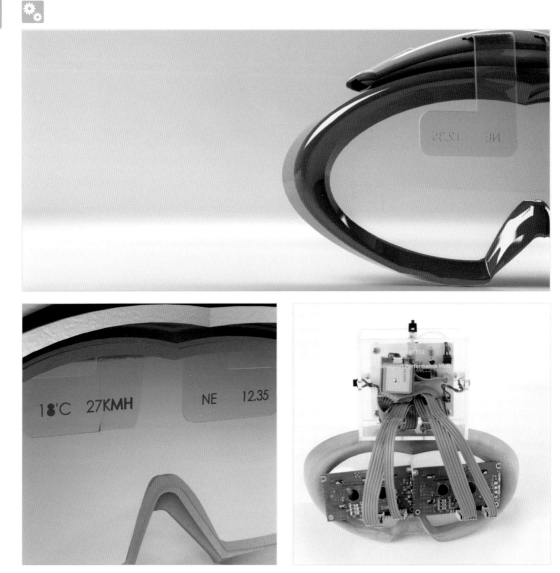

ViewData has been designed to combine a number of existing technologies in an intuitive high performance platform for snow sports practitioners.

The snow sports goggles with integrated GPS and transparent display technology provides skiers and snowboarders with a heads up display of performance data at the touch of a button. The embedded monitoring system keeps track of current speed, direction the time, ambient temperature and run time by means of a stopwatch.

During the design of the goggles, the number of components utilised in the intelligent portions of the device were minimised to optimise battery life and ensure that the form, fit and ergonomics of the goggles met existing standards and comfort levels established by already available winter sports eye wear.

Shaun Eldred

Product Design Engineering BSc

Also on p.108

Have you ever walked down the streets where you live at night and felt uneasy or even scared? These are not the emotions and sensations that should be associated with where you live. The solution is simple, and to illuminate the personal space where you are, it shows you what should and should not be avoided. Current street lighting does not achieve this well; there are small bright spots and dark wells in our suburban environments. Modern city centres are overrun by over bright lamps emitting light almost indiscriminately and have also given most night time urban environments a strange orange glow. This project uses light sources that give off light of a better whiter colour but are also not on for long periods when streets are empty. So these knee-high pathway lights meant for public walkways give off a better colour of light but also know when someone is walking along the path where they are positioned. They use a Passive Infrared Sensor as a trigger to switch from dim to bright. They then also send this information to the next lamp along the path thus lighting the path ahead of the person using it.

Sav Jeyendran
Product Design Engineering BSc

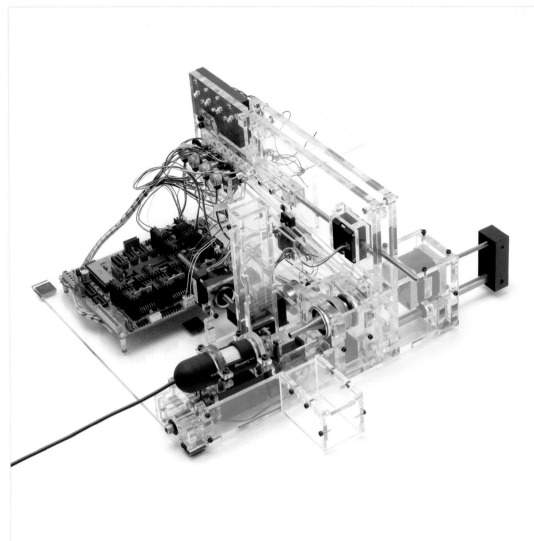

Inscentinel Ltd. is a biotechnology company, which specialises in harness the olfactory abilities of insects for trace vapour detection. The research carried out by Inscentinel focuses on using European honeybees for applications in home security, medical and quality control. The loading device automatically moves honey bees from a cage into Inscentinel's bee holders, which are used in the training device and hand held detector.

The bee loader operates by separating bees in to individual pods, queuing them for processing, changing their orientation and finally inserting them in to their holder. Video recognition is used to ensure the bees are correctly placed in their holders during the mounting operation. The bee loading device will ultimately be utilised by Inscentinel in conjunction with their bee training device and hand held detector in order to produce a commercial trace vapour detection system.

Adam Lambert
Industrial Design & Technology BA

Also on p.117

SliDex Performance Coating

Performance enhancing treatment for skis

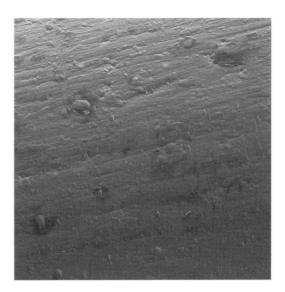

SliDex Performance Coating makes use of cutting edge thin film coating technology to provide ski treatment, which simultaneously reduces friction, and increases wear resistance. SliDex was the outcome of a project run in conjunction with Diameter Ltd that involved the careful balancing of materials science, engineering dynamics and design for usability.

SliDex exhibits a number of advantages over traditional ski wax including providing additional protection the ski base and not depositing oil based pollutants into the snow. In addition to the coating, the project developed the technology required to produce SliDex, test its performance and the tools required to apply the treatment accurately in a workshop environment.

Scanning electron microscopy image courtesy of Diameter Ltd.

Devraj Joshi
Product Design Engineering BSc

Also on p.110

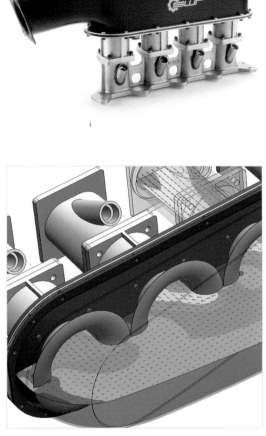

The brand RenaultSport is heralded as producing the most successful range of readily available performance vehicles of recent years. This project was focused on developing a direct replacement, performance enhancing intake manifold for the RenaultSport Clio F4R engine with the goal of measurably increasing the brake horse power and output torque.

After extensive theoretical and mechanical investigation, the manifold was developed to break free of the constraints imposed by the standard issue equivalent part. Additionally, the design process assessed factors affecting fitting, performance, durability and manufacture.

The manifold design was completed with full integration testing on a stock RenaultSport Clio conjunction with an ECU recalibration to fully maximise the design's performance enhancing effects. A combination of road, track and dynamometer tests confirmed the manifold's performance as a commercially viable product.

Tom Lewis
Industrial Design and Technology BA

Also on p.163

BlueDrop

Chlorine dosing for safe drinking water.

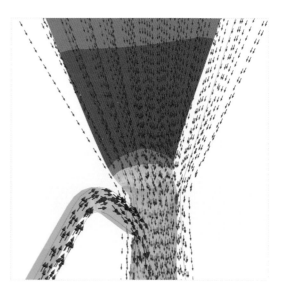

1.1 billion people still don't have access to safe drinking water. Adding chlorine is a cheap, safe and effective method of disinfecting dirty water and has been around for decades. However, the problem still remains due to expensive equipment and inaccurate mixing. This project tackled these issues and in collaboration with business and international development students, we aimed to turn this product into a social enterprise scheme.

The design drivers for this project were accuracy, reliability and cost. It catered to one of the most basic human needs in Maslow's hierarchy. This project looked at the fundamental technological options and economic manufacturing method to offer a design that could be produced in the country where it will be used.

Chlorine was chosen as the treatment method because not only is very affordable and quick, but it also offers continued protection for around 24 hours after initial disinfection, meaning any re-infection could be dealt with, for example, from a dirty cup or container.

James Bartlett

Industrial Design BSc

HyProtection
Hypothermia prevention device

This innovative and fashionable hypothermia prevention thermal top is for use in a cold harsh environment when the wearer may get injured, stranded or knocked unconscious, and not be able to move. Immobility allows hypothermia to set in a lot quicker as core body temperature drops rapidly.

A drop in core body temperature triggers a unique pattern of Sodium Acetate Trihydrate heat strips, creating an exothermic reaction thus warming up the body. HyProtection will allow the user more time to be found or get help before chronic hypothermia kicks in.

Thomas Le Mesurier
Industrial Design & Technology BA

Also on p.62

Hypo Hoist®

Man overboard recovery system - Design reg: 3020485, Trade Mark: 2408770

Hypo Hoist® is a rapid and efficient man overboard recovery system, specifically designed to save mariners' lives. It will rescue a casualty, conscious or unconscious out of the water and back onto the safety of the vessel, by the aid of just one person, whilst maintaining them in a constant horizontal position. It is vital to recover the casualty in this manner, because changing their attitude, and recovering them vertically, causes a rapid drop in blood pressure, which is already critically low due to cold shock syndrome, and significantly increases the risks of cardiac failure.

Hypo Hoist® has been in production with, Isle of Wight based marine specialist, SeaSafe Systems Ltd. since its international launch in 2006 and has received many national and international accolades for design, engineering and entrepreneurship. It is currently being tested and adapted for use on Royal National Lifeboat Institution vessels, and is being distributed across the world from various retailers. Due to the demand of the product SeaSafe Systems Ltd. opened a new 8000 sq ft factory in 2007 to accommodate the ever expanding Hypo Hoist® production line.

Tanya Louise Budd

Product Design Engineering BSc

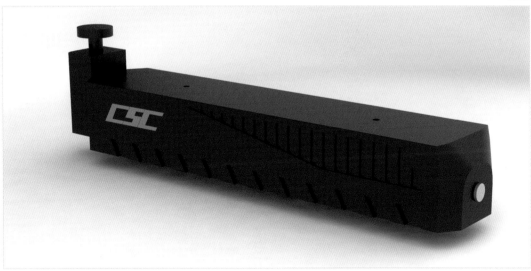

On an average day in London 23.8 Million journeys are made around and within the city. New ways of encouraging people to use the public transport network are greatly valued by governments and environmental agencies. The Chimera skate chassis was developed to encourage people to user more public transport by providing them with a device that speeds up the travel time between modes of public transport.

The chassis can be attached to a range of inline skate boots, allowing the user to skate to their mode of public transport before quickly disengaging the wheels to be able to walk. This gives the user a quick method of travelling to public transport and while not providing any drawbacks that are associated with current devices used for this context.

Chris Lynch
Industrial Design BSc

Also on p.63

S.H.A.R.D
Intuitive navigation for skiers and snowboarders

The S.H.A.R.D is a system developed to enhance the user's experience whilst skiing or snowboarding at mountain resorts. Digital information is overlayed onto the real world through the user's S.H.A.R.D goggles, providing them with exact locations of ski lifts, restaurants and other points of interest at the touch of a button. The system can then calculate the best suited route for the user depending on their skill level and guide them to their destination much like an in car sat-nav system. Friends and family with this system can also locate each other on the slopes and arrange meeting points and times. Other features include resort, weather and avalanche warning information as well as recording of statistical data such as altitude, speed and location. Routes can be pre-planned or altered on the go with this updated information able to be shared amongst other users.

Ultimately the purpose of this product is to remove uncertainty from skiing or snowboarding, helping users maximise their time on the slopes and spend it efficiently and safely.

Dan Sparrow
Industrial Design & Technology BA

Energy Harvesting Piezoelectrics

Rapture Assessment Device

A piezoelectric device will produce an electric charge when subjected to an appropriate strain.

This project investigated the use of a piezoelectric bimorph as a means of harvesting energy from a vibrating source. The vibration source used was a calibrated shaker and multimeters were used to measure electrical outputs. These outputs were then compared to the power inputs and the efficiency of the actuator was determined.

The aims of the project were to obtain experimental results and develop a greater understanding of parameter effects. Parameters included input power and vibration frequency; the most important of which was the vibration frequency where it was assumed that the actuator would generate its biggest output energy when it was vibrating at its natural frequency. The actuator itself consists of a cantilever piezoelectric bimorph, where the vibrations will shake the actuator and cause the bimorph to deflect and produce a charge. These actuators can theoretically be applied to any vibrating source to absorb the waste energy and produce a charge.

Atherosclerotic vascular disease is the most common cause of morbidity and mortality in the UK and the world as a whole. Atherosclerosis is the underlying cause major killer diseases such as heart attack and stroke.

The objective of my project is to design and fabricate a device for assessing the rapture of human arterial specimens. I strongly believe that this project has potential of breaking through into the market as viable product. I have completed the design for the device which is going to be used in the department of Biomedical Engineering at Brunel University. This tool would be used to perform the experiment to gather data necessary to study the behaviour of a lesion in a specimen under applied pressure forces. Its main use is to secure the specimen in position and allow fluid pressure to be applied and measure displacements until the specimen raptures. Stress in the arterial walls will be evaluated using the known, young modulus, size of specimen and final and displacement.

A new development in understanding the disease will enhance better management of the disease and enable new interventions aimed at prevention of the diseases. I am very grateful to have this opportunity to be working on this project, as it allows me to demonstrate some of the essential skills I gained during my studies at Brunel University.

Richard Burgess
Mechanical Engineering BEng

Richard Dune
Mechanical Engineering BEng

Remote Maze

A classic puzzle combined with modern technology

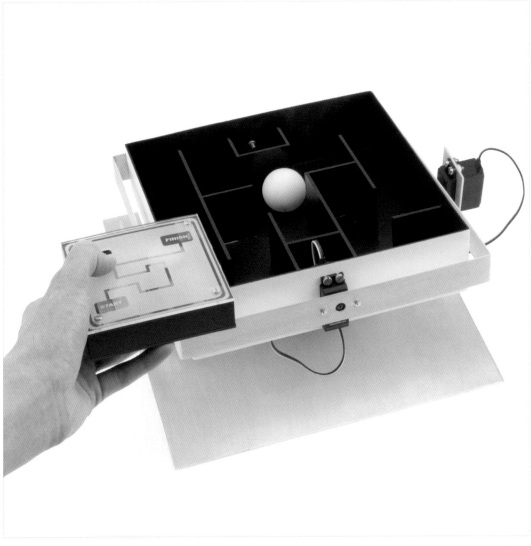

The ball bearing maze is a classic game that has entertained for years. Now with the introduction of new technologies it has become updated and state of the art. Remote Maze combines modern technology with the original game to provide a new challenge. By tilting the control unit the user must guide the ball to the end of the maze without touching it.

Using a blend of wireless communication, accelerometers and servo motors, the maze is moved through the use of a gimbal system. This controls the X and Y axis providing a full range of movement.

Daniel Beavis
Product Design BSc

Also on p.72

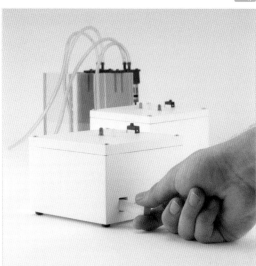

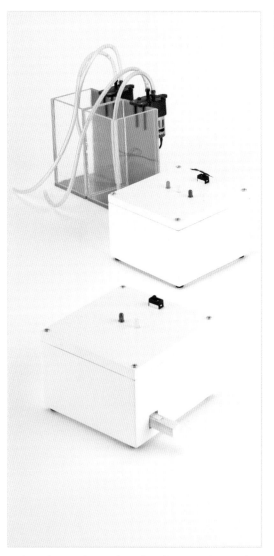

Swimming pools require a lot of care and attention and there are many areas within pool management that can cause a headache to the owner.

This system will automatically measure the pH levels of the pool and use appropriate counter measures to keep the pH levels of the water neutral.

The device includes an RGB reader that can differentiate between different PH strips. Once dipped into the water the strips are placed underneath the

sensor. If an Acid or Alkaline is detected then the sensor will wirelessly communicate to the second unit resulting in either an Alkaline or Acid balancer being pumped into the pool.

If the strip is deemed to be neutral then a white LED will turn on signaling no further action is required.

Richard Braine
Product Design BSc

Also on p.215

GPS Tracking Buggy
A small buggy which has the ability to follow anything

This product has the ability to follow whoever or whatever is holding the transmitting device. Utilising GPS technology within the transmitting device it is possible to tell the vehicle where to go, and how far to travel. If both parts of the product start in the same location it is possible for the user to move away and the buggy will follow them. Never again will you have to push your trolley around the supermarket, as it will be able to follow you. Never again will you need to look for your car keys as they will already be looking for you!

Integrating GPS into vehicles is no new feat, however this is not integrating it into a vehicle, this is integrating it into anything that moves. If the buggy was able to climb fences it would be able to follow your cat wherever it went! It is then possible to display the travelled journey on a graphic display on the transmitting device, so you know exactly where the device has been.

Shaun Eldred
Product Design Engineering BSc

Also on p.94

This Embedded System combines infra-red technology and microchip-controllers with mechanical movement to create a fun interactive two player game.

Two players battle against each other to achieve the highest score by consistently shooting closest to the centre of the target.

Player one takes aim whilst the second player rapidly moves the target from left to right, making it as hard as possible to hit the bullseye. Once player one has an empty magazine a score is calculated using infrared scanning technology. This is then transmitted wirelessly to an LCD screen on the remote control. Next it is player one's turn for revenge as the second player takes aim.

Michael Evans
Product Design BSc

Also on p.80

Seek_r

An adaptable robotics platform

Seek_r is an adaptable robotics platform comprising of all the support systems required for an autonomous rover.

The robot will automatically traverse an area, avoiding obstacles and reacting to other environmental variables as necessary. A telemetry link allows an operator to monitor Seek_r from a distance if required.

In the configuration shown, Seek_r is set up to use thermal imaging to locate candles in a room, approach them safely and blow them out using the front mounted fan. The modular peripheral bus allows sensors and devices to be swapped and interchanged for different tasks with ease.

Devraj Joshi
Product Design Engineering BSc

Also on p.98

Compiler
Identifying what grocery items need to be ordered

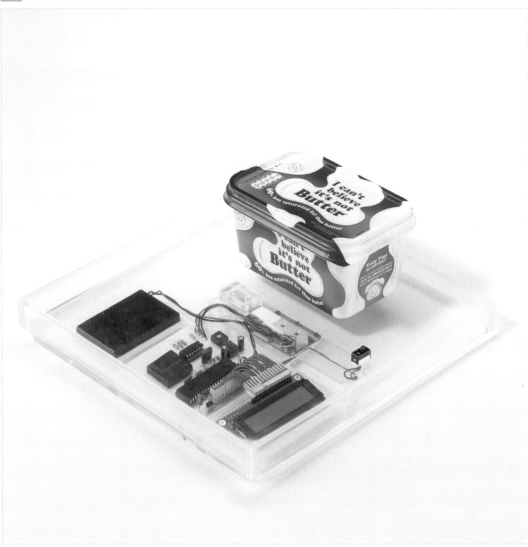

Shopping is a stressful activity especially when making lists, as there is always something that's missing or forgotten. Grocery shopping is one of the most repeated activities that occurs in day-to-day life. Complier aims to make shopping simpler and less stressful for our weekly grocery shop/order.

Compiler consists of a unit which can be adapted to be housed within a fridge shelf or a fridge door. Using RFID technology and a load sensor; Compiler scans and identifies the product as it is replaced within the fridge. Comparisons are made between its initial and current weight and will display on the units LCD if the item needs to be replaced, or its current quantity is acceptable.

The possibility of future developments include linking to the user's prefered shopping websites allowing products to be ordered automatically when quanities run low.

Samantha Mire
Product Design BSc

Also on p.70

This compact, high value, weather station gathers meteorological data remotely and transmits the external condition back to a base station. The core costs of the Weather Station have been carefully controlled to ensure that they fall within the most humble of student budgets whilst remaining sensitive and accurate to climate changes. As such, this project provides a cost effective solution to providing students with all the information they require to make informed choices about their behaviour; too cold for lectures today!

Matthew Perry
Product Design BSc

Also on p.82

Remote Control Tripod
Making photos level every time

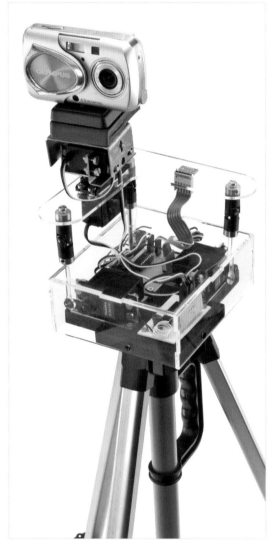

The remote control tripod is designed for use with digital still cameras. The pan and tilt functions of the tripod can be adjusted wirelessly from up to 50 metres away. This makes small adjustments in positioning a lot easier and more accurate, this is especially useful in macro photography.

The camera mounting plate is automatically levelled to a horizontal position to ensure that the camera is always set up level, this is controlled by an accelerometer and two servo motors.

A remote control tripod is very useful for wildlife photography as it allows you to adjust the angle and focus of the shot from a distance that will not interrupt the animal's natural behaviour, and it allows you to be much closer to the animals.

Tom Pilgrim
Product Design BSc

Also on p.205

The product is a reptile tank that connects to the Internet via a modem and downloads the weather and conditions for your reptile's natural environment. It gets the data for temperature, humidity, sunrise and sunset. The product then becomes automated with the UV lamps switching on and off at sunrise and sunset. The water is heated to the temperature for that day as well as the humidifier being set to low, medium or high depending on the current conditions. The tank also has a dirt sensor that measures if the tank is clean or not. When the tank is substantially dirty the sensor emits a signal which than send the user an email.

The product is intended for pet owners who want the best conditions for their pet and those that are scared of getting pets because of not being able to keep them in their natural environment.

Alexander Rincon
Product Design BSc

Tulipa Sermo Diligo

A voice-sensing desk plant that loves conversation

This desk toy reflects the mood in your office: In silence the flower will slowly close, but when there's conversation going on it slowly blooms. Try not to shout at it though, or it will get intimidated and snap shut. You can customise your flower's colour by clicking your favourite from a field of flowers growing from the bottom of your desktop.

The project demonstrates an embedded system centred around a PIC device. An amplified microphone provides the audio input, which is linked to a geared servo motor mechanism to open the petals. The colour setting is communicated over a USB link to the desktop computer, which changes the PWM settings for the flower's LED lighting. The flower is powered from the mains, and forms an interesting office novelty.

Eleanor Rogers

Product Design Engineering BSc

Also on p.216

This project involves the use of electrical and mechanical knowledge combined to create a simple table which will automatically level itself to hold a ball in a central position. The ball can be pushed around the table while it is automatically tracked and the angle of the table varied to put the ball back in the centre.

The table operates using a resistive touch and pressure sensor, attached to electronics with a micro controller at its heart. The micro controller is programmed with algorithms obtained through theory and trial and error in order to move the ball around the table and keep it steady in the centre.

Adam Lambert
Industrial Design & Technology BA

Also on p.97

McLaren Innovation
Carbon MonoCell MP4-12C.

At McLaren we are passionate about what we do; we have a unique vision of what that passion can achieve, and a burning ambition to succeed. Our new automotive company and, more specifically, the first of our new range of high-performance sports cars, the MP4-12C, is a classic example of what our passion and ambition can deliver. The 12C is set to re-write the rules of sports car design through Formula 1-inspired engineering, revolutionary chassis architecture and absolute focus on efficiency.

At McLaren, we have a rich history of innovation producing some of the most exciting and inspired car designs ever produced. Our automotive division has already built the world's most critically acclaimed supercar, the McLaren F1 (1993-1998) and the world's best-selling luxury supercar, the Mercedes-Benz SLR McLaren (2003-2009). McLaren Automotive now looks to the future with a new range of high-performance sports cars.

The innovative 12C and future models within the range, will challenge the world's best sports cars, benefiting from the expertise and virtuosity of the McLaren Group. Twenty years of sports car design, engineering and production combined with inspirational success in Formula 1 have been the driving force for the introduction of our ultimate line-up of technology-led and customer-focused performance cars for the 21st century. The rules in the sports car world are about to be re-written.

At its heart, the McLaren MP4-12C features a revolutionary carbon fibre chassis structure, the Carbon MonoCell: the first time a car in this market segment is based around such a strong and lightweight racing car engineering solution and the first time any car has ever featured a one-piece carbon fibre structure. This step change in sports car design means that the 12C introduces new standards not just in handling, ride and outright performance, but also safety, economy and practicality in an already competitive sector.

At McLaren, we have pioneered the use of carbon composite construction in the 1981 Formula 1 MP4/1 racing car, and set a trend that all Formula 1 teams have followed. On the road, carbon chassis have historically remained the preserve of the most expensive and exotic super cars; a purchase for the super-rich where costs are driven by the complexity of carbon fibre chassis design and build. The 12C challenges this by introducing the advantages of carbon composite – longevity, lightness of weight, high strength and torsional rigidity – to a more affordable sector through its revolutionary engineering as a one-piece moulding. Never before has a carbon fibre chassis been produced this way.

The 12C MonoCell weighs less than 80 kg. The use of carbon fibre contributes to the car's low overall weight and it forms the structural basis for the whole car. The torsional rigidity of the chassis is considerably stiffer than a comparable alloy structure. This inherent lack of flex means the unique front suspension system, which is mounted directly onto the MonoCell, requires less compromise for flex of the suspension itself. Therefore, it is easier to develop the unique balance between fine ride and precise handling that we at McLaren have always targeted.

The MonoCell also offers greater occupant safety. It acts as a safety survival cell, as it does for a Formula 1 car. Carbon composites do not degrade over time like metal structures that fatigue. The 12C will feel as good as new in this respect for decades and, even in the event of an accident, the lightweight aluminium alloy front and rear structures are designed to absorb impact forces; it can also be replaced with ease. Aluminium extrusions and castings are jig welded into the finished assembly and these are then bolted directly to the MonoCell.

In addition to the innovative chassis design, we have pioneered a new carbon fibre production process that allows the MonoCell to be produced to exacting quality standards, in a single piece, in only four hours. This compares favourably with the dozens of carbon components (and dozens of production hours) that normally feature in a carbon fibre chassis structure and naturally brings huge efficiency and quality benefits. Getting this production process right is the result of five years of extensive research and now the process is perfected, it allows us to produce the MonoCell repeatedly at very high quality.

The finished MonoCell emerges in one piece meaning that this new process could revolutionise car design. It avoids the need to bond different parts to make the whole structure, as with all other carbon fibre cars. It is hollow, saving further weight, and the integrity of production ensures the location of suspension and

ancillaries is accurate to the finest of tolerances. At McLaren, we have not just pushed the boundaries of design and engineering for performance and ride quality, we have redefined the chassis, using innovation and ingenuity to produce a driving experience that exceeds all expectations.

Achieving this revolutionary chassis design was no coincidence. It was the result of an extensive engineering-led design process including prototyping, testing and numerous simulations. At McLaren we have developed the most sophisticated Formula 1 driving simulator in the world. It is an immensely powerful tool and has been used extensively in the design and development process for the 12C, where modelling offers the opportunity to test likely outcomes without having to build a component that might turn out to be inadequate. It saves both money and time and it is perhaps the most effective technology transfer from Formula 1 to road cars. The crash test requirements are a good example of how

simulation helps speed up development. Long before the first Carbon MonoCell had been constructed, the design had been through hundreds of passive crash test simulations. When the time came to submit a real world crash test, the 12C passed with flying colours. Concise and considerate design solutions are at the heart of our ethos.

With the introduction of the 12C, McLaren is pushing Formula 1-inspired technology and the application of innovation into a whole new class, aiming not just to lead the field of sports-car engineering, but to redefine it entirely. The MonoCell embodies of McLaren innovation perfectly illustrating innovation that works.

By Ron Dennis CBE

Executive Chairman of McLaren Group and Executive Chairman McLaren Automotive

Technology With A Face
The Ups And Downs Of Social Computers.

It is human behaviour to act socially towards an interactive process, whether you are chatting to a character in an online world or having an argument with your Sat Nav. These social behaviours are hard wired within our brains and help us to react and engage with products in a way that we can understand.

Examples such as KITT from Knight Rider to Wall-E by Pixar, show how computers can be more than just lines of code and offer social cues as a means of breaking down complex user interaction.

However, breaking down computers into a social framework is nothing new, as the Apple Macintosh demonstrated in 1984. They changed the way people used and perceived the interface with the integration of office metaphors such as the recycle bin and the use of folders. The use of everyday social metaphors replaced the need for inputting lines of code that were difficult to learn and master. The social context of computers having a memory, reading files, or coming down with a virus, has become a continuous metaphor which allows us to rationalise functions or 'gremlins' within our computers.

By using these mental models for how humans communicate, designers and programmers endowed computers with human-like attributes allowing people to interact with complex technology with minimal anxiety or effort. This ability to put a face or add a familiarity to the technology then opened the market to a much wider audience.

However, sometimes interface designers do not get it right first time. Many people who grew up in the Microsoft Word era will remember with a shudder when a little paper clip bounced on screen followed by the infamous words: "Hello. It looks like you are writing a letter".

Offering the ability to help you format your documents, or even write Shakespeare, Microsoft's Clippit was a great leap in social technology. However, what started as a cute, novel little resource quickly became an intrusive pop-up seldom offering you help when you needed it.

Unfortunately the ability to mimic human behaviour magnified initial problems, with Clippit soon feeling like an annoying neighbour rather than a desktop tool. Admitting defeat Microsoft retired the little paperclip. Lessons learnt from this paradigm shift have inspired countless social actors since.

However, digital characters are not all bad: one popular example combines the use of keyboard symbols in the form of facial expressions and emoticons. As digital conversations are prone to being misread or misinterpreted, these simple cues such as a smiley face or wink adds both value and context to an otherwise detached statement. The popular colon-dash-parentheses can suddenly provide context and feedback to a conversation, suggesting that the preceding statement should not be taken seriously. ☺

This use of social technology allows us to communicate a tone of voice, or an expression – often the most commonly read signs in any good social interaction - that are conventionally lost during digital communication.

However, designers must be aware that the use of tone or metaphor within an artificial character can bring with it the power of social influence. The impact of "Oh dear John, you didn't get that one right" from a social actor is a vastly different effect to "Incorrect. Try again". Companies, realising this, have driven a rise in designs that help change our attitudes and behaviours. A prime example of this can be observed through persuasive design tactics: arming websites with social actors, pop-ups and metaphors to persuade us that Amazon.co.uk is just one click away.

Of course, websites have been using social technology since the nineties. The Lycos search engine, using a black Labrador as a social actor to 'Go get it' with regards to information. Lycos made good use of research into Human Computer Interaction (HCI) to make complex technology understandable. Lycos translated familar questions such as 'Where is Brunel?' into database queries to efficiently locate the website of interest. Such an approach questioned the need for people to understand the 'system' behind the dog when they would just enjoy the fact that if they asked him an everyday question, he would run off and find them the answer.

Similarly Ask Jeeves in 1996, built on this success to refine the use of 'natural language' when engaging with a technological tool. Both the clever use of user interface and playful roleplay, provided complex technology with a familiar face in what is now known as 'affective aspects' of computer interaction.

Before long, people forget that this social agent was in fact a series of commands and codes, and became at ease with his ability to answer questions just like a real human would. However, people then generate high expectations of these clever graphical user interfaces, on the basis that emulating human behaviour perhaps implies the ability to think and act like a human. Unfortunately when the public discover that a system is not as intelligent as they once thought, or perhaps is missing its 'empathy chip' they can quickly feel irritated or deceived.

Once disillusioned by such role-play, people tend to realise what the computer actually is: artificial. Obviously most people realise Jeeves is a computer, however with such convincing human-like qualities it would be hard for a techno-novice to tell the difference.

Through the use of social characters, natural dialogue and familiar metaphor, technology has allowed us to interact with computers with less anxiety and continued success. Often, people engage with these characters as if they were human and barely noticing when they are not. The depth and attention to detail in products such as Honda's ASIMO android, makes it increasingly difficult to imagine computers as just circuits and code as the face of technology continues to evolve.

By Ross Dudley

Why Did You Buy That?
Exploring the Psychology of Packaging

The supermarket today is a battleground for fast moving consumer goods. The shelves are filled with products and brands all fighting for the consumer's attention. This bombardment of choice makes people subject to impulsive decision-making: "Procter and Gamble believe that shoppers make up their mind about a product in about the same time it has taken to read this sentence" (The Wall Street Journal, 21st September 2005). The challenge for those seeking to win the battle amongst the shelves is getting noticed: in a world of excessive choice how can a product stand out?

The key is communication: aesthetically, digitally, functionally and emotionally. The frontline of consumer and product communication sits within the parameters of the product's packaging. Since the early 19th century, packaging was always viewed as having a functional purpose only needing to fulfil the role of protection and notification. Gradually, however, as the economy developed and goods became commoditised, the role of packaging began to change. In order to stand out from the abundance of generic choices on the shelf, companies began to innovate with their product ranges so that they could offer the consumer some customisation of choice. The incentive for consumers to buy into a brand was because that product and range offered a specific unique selling point (USP) over the competitors on the shelf. In order to communicate the USP of the product the role of the packaging became more dominant in its marketing. The packaging now had to act as a direct influence on the consumer's purchasing choice: a unique pack could stand out from the shelves and generate consumer interest. This method of engaging the consumer at the shelf became known as the First Moment of Truth (FMoT).

The idea of engaging a consumer at the shelf through the packaging is not new, in fact many companies integrated a sense of individualism long ago. Take companies such as Jack Daniels and Coca-Cola, both of which deliberately utilised a specific bottle type that became iconic to their individual product offering and brand. In both cases, the key to the bottle's success was the designer and manufacturer's understanding of aesthetical awareness. The uniquely designed bottle gave the product a strong visual image, leading to stronger promotional and marketing ties, inevitably leading to more successful FMoTs and sales.

Unfortunately, today the world of Fast Moving Consumer Goods (FMCG) is so overwhelmed with flamboyant and "unique" packs that the consumer has become desensitised to the impact; the shelves are full of "white noise". This phenomenon is known as "the paradox of choice". Barry Schwartz provides an interesting insight into this in his TEDtalk, suggesting that having too much choice paralyses the consumer through a sense of "well there are enough of them so I can't go wrong". The psychological implication of this is that the consumer then becomes less satisfied with their final product choice and the brand becomes homogenised into the same generic category as its competitors. The categories created by the consumer generally consist of a compromise between cost and perceived quality. The packaging techniques then help communicate to the consumer which category it should fit within. For example, give a consumer a pack of a store branded "economy" tea bags and a pack of Twining's tea bags and ask them to comment on the two. They will generally suggest that the Twining's bags are of a higher quality, despite not having physically tried the goods inside. However, give the consumer a choice between a premium supermarket brand that has been packaged similarly to the Twining's then the consumer values both of the products in the same light and uses the price to establish the quality level. The abundance of choice has distilled the power of packaging communication: no longer are consumers drawn to a single product but to a group of "generic possibilities". In terms of packaging design this makes the ability to win FMoTs even more important and also more complicated. If consumers' choices are distorted by the overwhelming aesthetics on a shelf, how can a product stand out?

In-order to stand out from the competition packaging designers need to consider the consumer's decision-making process. Behavioural studies show that consumers operate within four groups:

- Cognitive reactions are based on the exploitation of sensory or emotive stimuli to engage the consumer.
- Learning reactions are associated with the consumer's previous experience with the product and brand.
- Refinement links with the learning model but involves decisions that have been influenced by the product's environment, placement, offers and so on.

- Habit refers to consumers who make choices based on their own institutionalised views, either based on experience or word of mouth. These consumers often display entrenched behaviour patterns.

By understanding and innovating around these models the designer can produce packs that have a new type of uniqueness that stands out from the white noise. Daz detergent packaging, for example, uses AromaRelease technology to "print" the detergent fragrance into the pack. This provides the pack with a cognitive edge as consumers become fully aware and attracted by the smell enticing them to make a purchase over the "generic" branded packs. Packaging design is based on providing "pleasant surprises" over the competitors.

Cognitively designed smarter packs may be successful in generating consumer interest on the "frontline" in the supermarket, but the process falls into the same trap as previous packaging innovations, which is that at some point the packaging leaders will be caught up by the other companies and the white noise of the shelf will intensify causing more confusion in product selection. This suggests that in order to win the consumer over a deeper level of innovation needs to be implemented which coincides with the behavioural models. The designer needs to consider the importance of the FMoT in future: will it be as prominent in the consumer's decision-making process when the other models are not based on aesthetic, decision-making but are controlled by elements of consumer experience and opinion?

Over the past decade the Internet has revolutionised the way the world works, transforming the way consumers think and in so doing it has a definite impact on the importance of and direction of packaging innovation. Arguably the Internet as a shopping medium has rendered the development of innovative packaging pointless: what good is the Daz pack when it is has been limited to a couple of pixels? The Internet has created a huge shift in packaging design intentions, so that with smarter consumers and digital constraints the focus of FMoTs has shifted. Digital consumers are no longer influenced by the smell and colour of a product but are most likely to select goods based on a refinement level, whatever is at the top of the online "hit list"; a learning level, based on personal experience with previous purchases; or

habit levels where they will buy goods dependant on recommendations. Essentially the digital market as well as factors such as the economic downturn, have caused consumers to become focussed on "thoughtful spending", thus reducing the impact of aesthetically, cognitively pleasing packs on the shelf and a reduction in impulse based decision-making.

By Joe-Simon Wood

Hydration Refuelling Station
Future concepts for Armitage Shanks

A conceptual product for Armitage Shanks that minimises personal dehydration issues throughout the day. In the future, keeping hydrated will be a primary health concern. Many consumers often neglect their body's need for water and the lack of free, fresh, public water is a problem.

Armitage Shanks offer a solution; The Hydration Refuelling Station. Capitalising on a growing trend of 're-usable' drinking bottles, this innovative water fountain breaks preconceptions of traditional public

facilities, offering a hygienic and safe way to consume pure distilled water. Perfect for busy shopping centres, leisure centres and hotels, this product is aesthetically pleasing and functionally acute.

People can 'log-in' to view their daily water habits and recommendations of how to stay healthy. Also in the context of water shortages this can be used for the allocation and monitoring of water consumption in collaboration with the government.

Mitch Neofytou
Industrial Design BSc

Also on p.21

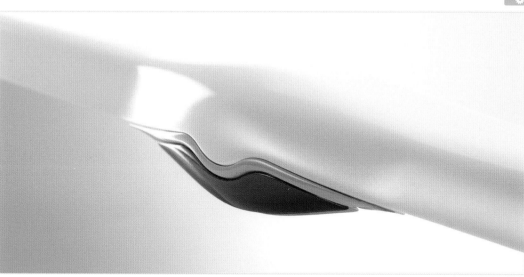

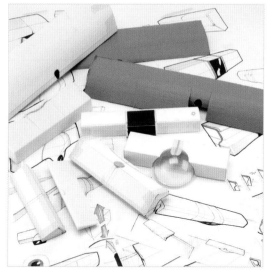

A conceptual product for Armitage Shanks that focuses on the personal health of homeowners, bringing healthcare and a new health regime into our home.

An encyclopedic medical database that uses facial recognition technology to assess the user's health is embedded within an interactive mirror. Illnesses that require urgent medical attention are prioritised with immediate importance, whilst illnesses that require a change in the user's diet can be instantly recommended. Touch screen technology enables the user to interact with their health providing an increased communicative experience. Armitage Shanks offer an effective and convenient health monitoring system to maintain wellbeing on a day to day basis.

Also on p.87

Jon Walmsley
Industrial Design BSc

Escalator Handrail Sanitation
Future concepts for Armitage Shanks

A conceptual service for Armitage Shanks providing cleaner public spaces.

Escalator handrails are a breeding ground for germs and parasites. Two million people use escalators on the London Underground system every day and 80% of germs are transferred through hand contact.

The Armitage Shanks escalator sanitation unit safely and hygienically cleans the handrail. This reduces the risk of cross infection between users, improving commuter confidence daily.

Chris Place
Industrial Design & Technology BA

Also on p.84

Personal Health Information System
Future concepts for Armitage Shanks

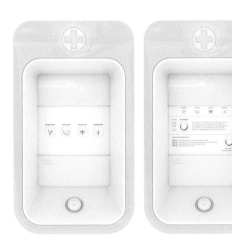

A conceptual service for Armitage Shanks that enables personal health management.

In the year 2025 over population in the UK will be a major contributor to the spread of diseases. As a result, systems to help control, increase awareness and prevent transmission of infections in public areas will generate improved public health.

This conceptual Armitage Shanks product provides personal health feedback via portals located in key public venues. A touch screen interface with bio sensory testing equipment enables people to measure their health levels and receive information regarding the best ways in which to improve it. The concept works alongside a public health database with personalised user profiles, made accessible via the Internet. Health tests will be logged on the database to show development over time. This would be accessible for not only the user but for NHS and private health services. This portal gives the public control over their personal health information.

Francis Lofthouse
Industrial Design BSc

Also on p.195

A conceptual service for Armitage Shanks that minimises the spread of infectious diseases.

As the global population continues to grow, overcrowding will become prevalent within urbanised areas. Society will be forced to live and work in urban megacities where compacted environments will be vulnerable to the vicious spread of disease and infection. Armitage Shanks is taking responsibility for addressing future issues through equipping people to look after themselves in this hostile world.

Hand sanitation is a necessary requirement for the fight against infectious diseases. The concept being developed focuses on bringing quick, convenient hand sanitation to the masses within their public domain. Incorporating future UV technology, the solution will be an aesthetically appealing form that subtly represents the product's functionality thus adhering to Armitage Shanks' core values.

Charlie Cooke
Industrial Design & Technology BA

Also on p.29

Titan Portable Sound System
Future design concepts for Cambridge Audio

Music throughout the ages has been considered a form of relaxation and escapism, transporting people away from their everyday lives into a paradise of their creation. In today's bustling society where our senses are being assaulted from all flanks, the ability to switch off and escape has never been more desirable.

Cambridge Audio, a British Hi-Fi institution, has an opportunity to expand their stable prosumer base of audiophiles with a new range of products. The Titan headphones create a macro environment where the user can feel fully connected to their music. The product embodies the design ethos of Cambridge Audio and fully encapsulates the brand's identity. Consisting of two complementary components; a dock and headphones, the Titan removes the traditional hassles of MP3 players, releasing the user from the tentacle-like grasp of cables and cords. Users can simply transfer their most cherished audio experiences directly to the Titan headphones.

Rebecca Doggett
Industrial Design & Technology BA

Also on p.26

The increase in digital music over the last few years looks set to grow in the future, with ever-developing download sites becoming more accessible. This means demand for music storage and visual manipulation of digital media is growing. However current products do not allow the user to listen to their music on Hi-Fi's systems without having to plug in external MP3 players. This creates an inferior interface and a less than satisfactory aesthetic appearance.

This unique and innovative system allows the user to store, view and manipulate digital music at will, with no need for a computer or MP3 player. The device auto-updates by downloading music wirelessly from a PC. Music can be streamed via the product using available online programs. It encompasses traditional tactile responses which are synonymous with current Cambridge Audio Hi-Fi's, and gives a visual illusion of having a shelf full of traditional media like CD's. Its unique yet stylish aesthetic looks at home alongside other high end Hi-Fi systems.

Simon Warne
Industrial Design & Technology BA

Also on p.88

Hearing Aid
Future design concepts for Cambridge Audio

Cambridge Audio is a company renowned for developing innovative and technologically advanced audio equipment. They pride themselves on providing reasonably priced sound systems and ensure that only the finest quality materials and electronic components are used in every beautifully designed product.

'Hearing Aid' takes into consideration the rate at which our population is ageing and the damage caused by the continual use of poor headphones in conjunction with loud music. Hearing loss is a serious issue that continues to grow and will affect a large number of the future population. New hearing aids that are skillfully designed and electronically superior will improve everyday lives helping to provide users with perfect audio clarity.

Norah Lewis
Industrial Design & Technology BA

Also on p.31

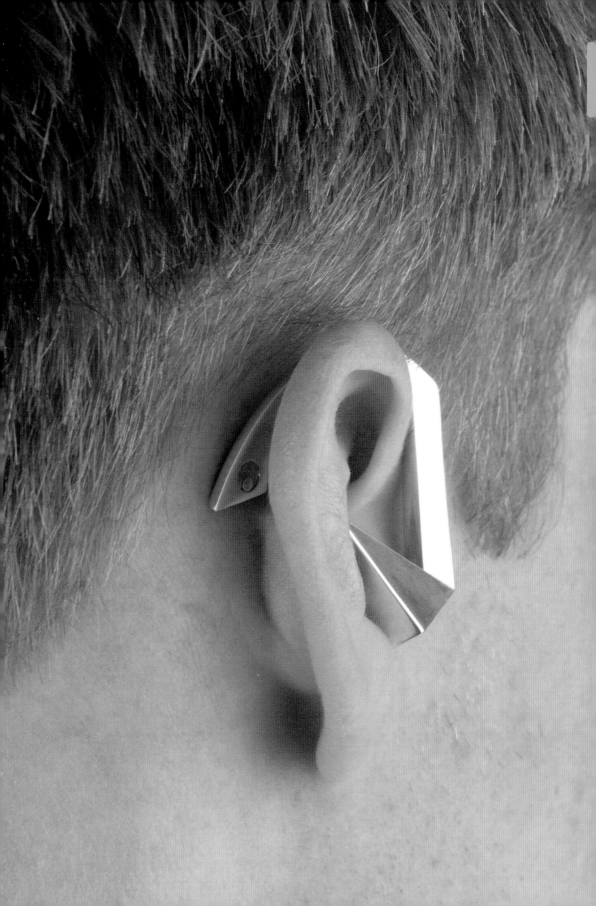

Outside Audio System
Future design concepts for Cambridge Audio

This portable sound system is designed to be used outside to maximise your outdoor music experience.

The product has brushed Aluminium speaker components. The touch screen within the two speakers is revealed or hidden by opening and closing the speakers. It is operated as soon as your finger touches the screen and then allows you to scroll through and select the music stored in the hard drive that you wish to listen to.

At the top of the cylinders there are touch sensitive buttons flush with the speaker; these operate the speaker functions available within the product.

The sophisticated and sleek aesthetic marks this out as a product in line with Cambridge Audio's high quality brand. Freeing users from the need to be at home in order to experience high audio clarity. The Outside Audio System is therefore ideal for picnics and pursuits.

Victoria Grantham
Industrial Design & Technology BA

Also on p.189

How much is your favourite song worth? What return do you receive for your invisible 79 pence?

The Record is a portable medium for holding music that provides a tangibility which digital downloads lack in abundance. Each Record encompasses data storage and a gorgeous OLED screen in a precious metal base. Every Record is unique and stores a single album, which can never be transferred, formatted or copied. This essence of permanence affords the user strong physical and emotional connections to the individual elements in their music collection. Multiple records may be interlocked magnetically, creating a spanned display and an artefact greater than the sum of its parts. A collection of records is the music, the playlist and the interface.

The Armature is a universal audio player capable of playback from a wide gamut of storage media. The glass surface with integrated OLED display offers an intuitive touch based interface for managing, linking and visualising songs as they play.

Tom Wakeling
Product Design BSc

Also on p.35

3D 720
Future design concepts for Kodak

With a consumer and industry zeitgeist for high definition imaging more and more manufactures are turning to super thin, high efficiency OLED flat screen technologies to provide the colour fidelity and image clarity that the market demands. With the recent introduction of consumer grade 3D vision systems for the home viewing experiences are set to become all the more immersive.

The Kodak Closer 3D 720 offers new ways of sharing and displaying visual information. By synthesising a number of existing technologies into a portable form factor, this concept provides a platform for portable holography based on OLEDs. The product form and casing remains faithful to a traditional lens case, something deeply engrained in the Kodak brand.

Nick Salpingidis
Product Design BSc

Kodak's expanded values revolve around the enrichment of friendships and family life. Assisting individuals in maintaining and improving their quality of life is core to this endeavour. Kodak's Album aids users by preventing stress and combating depression, ensuring a good level of mental health and the psychological well being associated with connecting with those you are fond of.

Kodak Album is packed with features that will allow users to capture, record, share and display their special moments. Album is also a personal guardian, constantly monitoring its owner's health in case of emergency.

Vasapol Kittipol
Industrial Design & Technology BA

Closer

Future design concepts for Kodak

Closer is a new development for Kodak's product portfolio. Recently, Kodak has shifted its focus away from consumer products and into the commercial arena. Closer aims to bring Kodak back to prominence in the consumer market.

This new 360 degree, 3D, high definition projector aims to create an all encompassing imaging experience for all. The use of declined lenses allows the reproduction of 3D images without requiring projector pairs on each side of the device.

Aleksandrs Malcevs

Industrial Design & Technology BA

Also on p.24

Life Logger
Future design concepts for Land Rover

For 60 years and more Land Rover have remained a prominent part of British heritage, helping all over the world in exploration, protection, combat, outdoor enjoyment or simply supporting family values. The project looked into the Defender brand and as changing laws threaten the future of the vehicle, examining the way Land Rover will retain the crucial elements of its design language.

As technology advances the ability to store memories will become more achievable. Photos will remain core as we visually keep a record of an event, but we will also be able to record the smell, the sound and the emotion associated with the picture giving a 3D or even 4D feel. The Life Logger represents the way Land Rover would use this technology and travel with you wherever you may venture, protecting those memories for you, gathering and storing them until you wish to view them. Whatever happens your memory is protected by Land Rover. You can put your life in its hands and trust that it will be there forever.

Ben Boutcher-West
Industrial Design & Technology BA

Also on p.183

This product is aimed at users who love the outdoors, or work outdoors. It is a way of taking the comfort of a home-cooked lunch out and about wherever you want to go. The product is designed to keep the food inside at the optimum temperature until you eat and enjoy.

The Lunch Rover has been designed to be included in a range of products for Land Rover that complement the Defender vehicles. Based on the company values, the Lunch Rover is robust, ready for anything and made to be used. Wherever it goes it leaves its mark without harming the environment.

The Lunch Rover uses all the defining aesthetics of Land Rover, will get your lunch through hell and high water, and deliver it unharmed and at perfectly controlled temperature when it is needed.

Louisa Santilli
Industrial Design & Technology BA

Also on p.83

Fortress
Future design concepts for Land Rover

With increased public demand for the security and data protection on Hard Disk Drives (HDD), and the dependency people have on these relatively small devices, the ability to safely haul around a HDD is a highly desired product concept.

With the Land Rover Fortress, it is possible to own a data storage device that will never fail and can be used anywhere. The connections from the product to the computer are such that the person using it will never be worried about loose cables and disconnection.

Fortress is impregnable from accidental drops and knocks. The drive has no specific orientation so people can use it how they see fit. The inclusion of extra features (such as data transfer lights) make every action performed by the drive obvious to the owner.

The Land Rover Fortress protects your data better than any other available hard drive. It makes you aware of what it is doing. It is secure when transferring data. You can trust your most valuable documents, photos and media to it and it will never let you down.

Andrew Morley
Industrial Design BSc

Also on p.286

The world's surface has been explored by Land Rovers and the time now comes to consider new opportunities. As the world progresses to sustainable design Land Rover aims to lead the application of new technologies in extreme environments in the essence of the Defender.

Replicating the Defender's reliability and versatility the generator converts the air around us into electrical power sources. No other fuel sources are required and no harmful by-products are produced. The generator will operate in rugged and demanding environments from third world countries to disaster zones, but will not be out of place in the home for emergencies.

The range of applications require the generator to be universal in its deliverables and so facilitates for charging electrical devices such as laptops and mobile phones, car chargers for Sat Nav systems and domestic plug sockets for power tools. All connections also have variable voltages to enhance international usage.

Russell Anley
Industrial Design & Technology BA

Also on p.90

Connect
Future design concepts for Red Bull

The Red Bull Connect grants users access to entire communities at the touch of a button. Expanding social horizons for all, Connect facilitates interaction between anyone. Having created an online profile, Connect allows users to find others with similar interests within the community and who would love nothing more then to meet someone new.

Nathan Brown
Industrial Design & Technology BA

Also on p.73

Vivid samples the audio, visual and olfactory facets of an experience allowing users to capture their adventures in a new and holistic way. Using a projector to recreate videos and images as well as an olfactory stimulator and adaptive surround sound Vivid is capable of recreating adventures and experiences. By allowing people to share their lives in this way, Vivid strives to inspire others to go on their own adventures and explore the word around them.

Jamie Gunton
Industrial Design & Technology BA

Also on p.200

Active
Future design concepts for Red Bull

The Red Bull Active is an activity searching and planning tool, which can be used from the confines of an office cubicle. By providing parameters such as distance, cost, activity type and skill level, Active will seek out and list options for adventures in order of relevance.

Flipping the unit over, users may view a calendar of planned activities and if desired full details about the activities they have planned.

Eoghan Power
Industrial Design & Technology BA

Modeled on a traditional orienteer's map holder, the Red Bull Freedom is an intuitive OLED based map designed to assit people in their exploration of the undiscovered world around them.

Freedom is designed to plan walking routes and guide ramblers whilst they trundle around interesting landmarks, unique spots of natural beauty and viewpoints for photography. The product monitors the progress of walking groups suggesting detours and the like as they traverse their routes. Routes become more scenic and adventurous as walkers become more experienced; Freedom travels with hikers from the smallest steps through to the highest peaks.

At home, Freedom docks with a base station transforming in to a digital photo frame, displaying images of completed journeys and teaser images of potential walks to come.

Winner of the 2010 MEX Student User Experience Award

Adrian Bliss
Industrial Design & Technology BA

Also on p.182

Breathing Mask for the Police Force
Future design concepts for Samsonite

Law enforcement officers strive to protect us, but need to be properly supplied with the equipment to keep them safe in the hazardous environments they often encounter. This breathing mask concept, developed for Samsonite, aids breathing in noxious environs. It makes use of the brand's ethos of protection and material innovation to form the perfect breathing mask. Police need to be able to rely upon their equipment without a second thought; they need to feel confidence in it so that they can give their full attention to the complex situation in hand. The aesthetic follows a sleek, purpose-driven form familiar to Samsonite products. Using investigation into advanced materials and features, the breathing mask was designed to be perfectly suited to its environment, and to be the best available solution for the user group. The design takes into consideration the psychological cues required to convey the sense of authority a law enforcement officer requires to perform their job. The mask demonstrates an understanding of user requirements whilst providing an innovative solution to extreme work-related hazard.

Bradly Hood
Industrial Design & Technology BA

Also on p.202

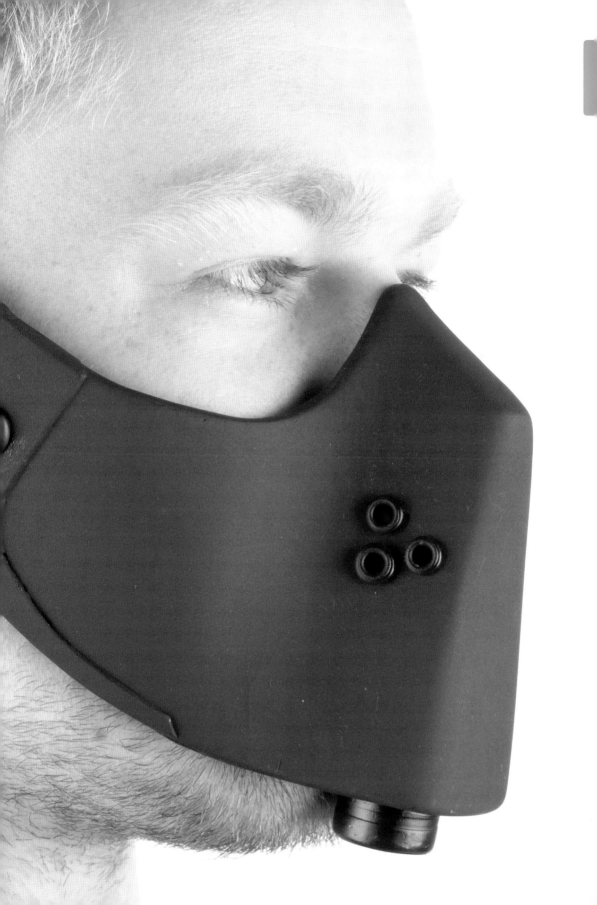

Fire Hose Guide Aid
Future design concepts for Samsonite

The Samsonite Flow is a hose retention system that has been ergonomically designed to relieve the backpressure that fire hoses exert when pumping water at high pressure. During dangerous operations, supporting the hose improves manoeuvrability and reduces fatigue, allowing fire fighters to concentrate on their vital work.

The device gives maximum support to the backpressure of the hose using a large ergonomically shaped pad, which sits around the fire fighter's midsection. The user then clamps the device down onto the hose using their lower arm, holding it securely in place at all times. By spreading stress across the midsection and away from the wrists and forearms, the fire fighter is given better control over the hose, reducing the risk that it will be dropped. The form was developed through a functional ergonomic approach, and various styling aspects typical of the Samsonite brand, finished in a matt black and bright orange combination which allows the device to be easily recognized during difficult operations.

Chris Holloway
Industrial Design BSc

Also on p.77

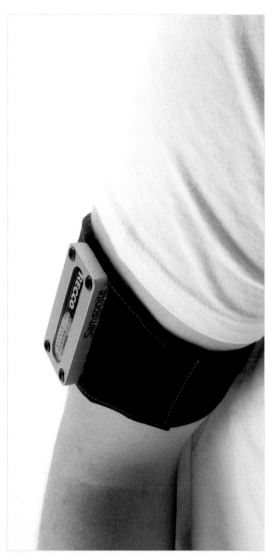

Approaching the concept of protection from a different angle, the Detect Strap is a device that allows emergency detection of an individual involved in a remote or dangerous role. The underclothing arm strap integrates Samsonite's knowledge of materials, alongside the proven detection technology of Recco's avalanche rescue systems.

The lightweight and durable design of the strap is combined with a maintenance-free detection system to create a "fit and forget" product which helps professionals feel secure and able to concentrate on the job at hand without worry.

Also on p.99

Tom Lewis
Industrial Design & Technology BA

Peripheral Falling Object Warning Device
Future design concepts for Samsonite

Expanding the Samsonite brand into the protection industry, this unit is designed to attach to a standard safety helmet of the type used worldwide. Safety helmets are present in all types of diverse situations, however all of them share the potential danger of being hit on the head by a falling object. A system delivering a pre-warning or sense of what is happening above greatly reduces this danger. The proposed product achieves this by residing a periphery of the user's vision, not imposing on the main field of view, but giving a view of the area directly above the user through a fish eye lens and fibre optics. As human peripheral vision is sensitive to motion detection, the reaction speed is very high, often bypassing the user's central processing system to prompt an instant response, giving this product an edge over traditional alerts such as buzzers and flashing lights. The product is ruggedly designed for daily use in both ordinary and extreme situations, and its durability is representative of the Samsonite brand.

Matt Keylock
Product Design Engineering BSc

Samsonite has found itself re-emerging from bankruptcy and needs to expand its market in order to become financially stable. Being famed for protecting travel goods, it is time to expand this concept to the next level: protecting people. Focusing on the construction industry, which is the most dangerous land-based work sector in Europe, it is important to note that not all countries have high health and safety precautions like the UK. With the exponential rise in the global population, together with mass urbanisation, it is vital to improve safety equipment for construction workers. Especially for those working in skyscraper sites where the risk of falling objects – such as a small bolt – could prove to be fatal.

A gap in the market has allowed for the development of Cliptite; a neck protecting add-on for the everyday construction helmet. The incorporation of the innovative material d3o makes the design lighter and safer, and the product builds on an industrial bond that could strengthen all of Samsonite's future products.

Luiza Frederico
Industrial Design & Technology BA

Also on p.22

At McLaren, a passion for design and technology constantly drives us to improve performance and never settle for anything less than the best. It is for this reason that we are delighted to be associated with Made in Brunel: Innovation that works as we recognise in their student team this same spirit and commitment to excellence.

Made in Brunel is a shining example of the commitment, passion and talent of some of the best engineering and design students in the UK and from across the globe.

Ron Dennis CBE

Brunel Racing
Brunel University Formula Student Race Team

In 2009 Brunel Racing entered Formula Student UK, Silverstone and Formula Student Germany, Hockenheim.

Formula Student UK saw the team produce its best result in 7 years since BR-3 came 4th in 2002. Solid results throughout all events put Brunel Racing in a good position for the toughest test of the competition, the Endurance event. Despite the torrential rain, Andrew Bonjour and Rob Still posted consistently fast laps throughout the event to finish fourth. Combined with an excellent third-lowest fuel consumption, Brunel Racing outscored the entire grid to climb to 6th place overall in the competition. The final results showed an extremely close tie between positions 4, 5 and 6 with Brunel Racing finishing 0.4 points behind fifth place Helsinki Metropolia UAS and 1.6 behind fourth-placed top UK team, Team Bath Racing.

Two weeks later Brunel Racing joined 77 other teams at the Hockenheimring, Germany, and continued its earlier success. The team excelled throughout the competition posting 5th place in both the Acceleration and Skid-pad events and finishing 7th in the Business Presentation event. The Endurance track was particularly hot and bumpy harsh conditions, which resulted in two thirds of the competitors suffering mechanical failures meaning that they were unable to finish. Brunel Racing's car, BR-X, was not immune to the conditions and lost several seconds a lap due to rear suspension failure. However Rob Still and Andrew Bonjour were able to prove their driving ability by continuing to drive the car to finish the race in 19th place.

An overall result of 16th at Formula Student Germany, in addition to the 6th place achieved at Silverstone, ended Brunel Racing's most successful season to date and saw the team climb over 141 places to 38th in the world.

BR-XI Design Overview

Brunel Racing's 2010 car, BR-XI, is the team's 11th consecutive entry to Formula SAE's Class 1 and builds upon the experiences and successes of previous years. With great emphasis placed on mass reduction over previous designs as well as increased power and additional driving control technology, BR-XI is expected to be competing for silverware when the team compete at Silverstone in July and Hockenheim in August.

Chassis

BR-XI features an aluminium honeycomb sandwich monocoque and rear spaceframe hybrid. The monocoque at the front provides a neat and sleek appearance to the car while the steel spaceframe at the rear has made it simpler to package the complex powertrain and fuelling systems and also increases access for maintenance and repairs. The aluminium honeycomb sandwich panels have an excellent stiffness to weight ratio and have allowed the team to produce a fully equipped car that weighs only 200kg.

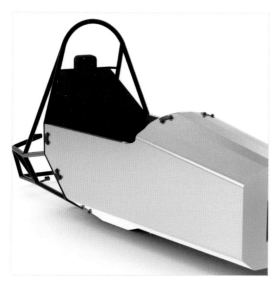

Suspension

Suspension geometry has been designed using Optimum K, a dedicated kinematic analysis program, in conjunction with test data obtained from a series of tyre tests with Brunel Racing's 2009 car, BR-X. A highly adjustable suspension system has been created through the incorporation of anti-roll bars, interchangeable springs and application specific 3-way adjustable dampers. Finite Element Analysis has been used to minimise component weight whilst still achieving sufficient strength and stiffness. Particular attention has been paid to camber loss due to compliance and deflection of components during cornering and braking.

Powertrain

A 2007 Yamaha YZF-R6 engine powers BR-XI and despite a mandatory intake restrictor the modified and tuned engine produces in excess of 90bhp to give BR-XI an impressive power to weight ratio of 470bhp per tonne. BR-XI's intake and exhaust systems have been designed to minimise flow restrictions and make efficient use of the limited air available for combustion while still providing effective inertia tuning. As such, a bespoke double-barrel type throttle has been designed that provides no restriction to the airflow at wide-open-throttle.

Brunel Racing
Brunel University Formula Student Race Team

Drivetrain

The drivetrain has been designed with an ultra lightweight clutch type limited slip differential and bespoke designed driveshafts and joints. The design includes equal length driveshafts and outboard CV joints that are housed within the rear hubs which reduce the operating angle of the driveshafts and increase component lifespan. Multiple final drive sprockets have been manufactured to provide a choice of three different final drive ratios depending on the specific event type or track conditions.

Team Details

Simon Dingle	Team Principal
Yannick Cheung	Testing & Simulation
Andrew Haughton	Chassis & Controls
James Stephens	Powertrain
Andrew Bonjour	Unsprung Group
Daniel Sheard	Drivertrain & Bodywork

Driver Aides

Some of BR-XI's greatest strengths are the advanced driver aide technologies that are featured in its design. Electronic semi-automatic gear-shifting and a servo clutch system with anti-stall are actuated via steering wheel mounted paddles allows the driver to keep both hands on the wheel at all times and removing the need for a foot clutch. These new features, in addition to adjustable launch and traction control make BR-XI easy to drive on the limit.

Brunel X-Team

An electric motorcycle for the Isle of Man TTZero competition.

Background

In September 2008, four final year students from the Mechanical Engineering subject area set out to design and build a high performance electric motorcycle. Guided by a core team of academic staff, the result was the Brunel X-team and the BX-09, a supersport prototype bike based on a Triumph Daytona 675 donor chassis with a single DC motor and a bespoke 72V Lithium-Ion battery pack.

In June 2009, with no prior track testing or dynamometer characterisation, the BX-09 was taken straight from the lab to the open roads on the Isle of Man, just in time to enter the world's first low carbon motorcycle grand prix competition, the Time Trials Extreme Grand Prix or TTXGP. The gruelling Isle of Man TT course is 37.73 miles long and is famous for its country roads and steep inclines and, especially,

the mountain section, which rises above the tree line and climbs to a height of approximately 1400ft.

Following an eventful week of practice and scrutineering, pro-rider Steve Harper put down an outstanding result on race day with the BX-09 for the Brunel X-team. Out of 22 entries, there were 13 starters and Harper finished 6th out of the Pro class and 9th overall. In fact, the Brunel X-team was the only UK university to finish the lap. Moreover, as the only university entrant in the Pro class, the BX-09 stood its ground against multi-million dollar company bikes from the US and some very experienced inventors from UK, Europe and India.

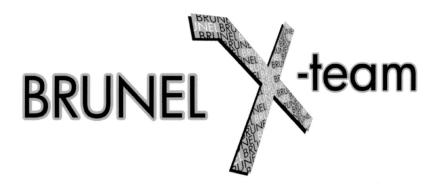

BX-10 Specifications

Drive Train
-Motor: dual brushed DC
-Peak power: 28kW/motor
-Transmission: single gear direct drive

Power Source
-Kokam Lithium-Polymer Prototype Cells
-84V bespoke battery pack and monitoring systems

Performance Estimates
-Top speed 120mph
-Avg speed 85mph
-Mass 200kg

Team Details

IoM Race Team:
Edmund Bright	Crew Chief
Adam White	Battery Systems
Timothy Clarke	Battery Systems
Gregory Da Santos	Motors and Control

Campus Support Team:
Mohamed Abukar	Motor Analysis
Rajveer Lotay	Thermal Analysis
Stephen Kago	CAD and Data Analysis

Rider
Paul Owen	Pro-rider Team 98 Racing

Project Supervision:
Dr Koen Matthys	Team Manager

Join the excitement and follow the team at
www.brunelx-team.co.uk

2010 Challenge

Following on from the success on the Isle of Man and delivering on expectations to improve for 2010 was no mean feat. Yet, exactly that was the challenge taken on by seven Level 3 project students from the Mechanical Engineering subject area this year, as they gave rise to the all-new 2010 Brunel X-team.

With the DNA of the BX-09 as a sound foundation, they set out to create a vastly improved prototype bike, the BX-10. As its predecessor, the BX-10 has been purpose built for racing on the Isle of Man TT course. This year, the second running of the Isle of Man electric motorcycle race is reformatted as the TTzero event and has been given an official slot on the TT race week calendar. BX-10 will have its race outing on 9 June with pro-rider Paul Owen and will benefit from a dual DC motor configuration and a bespoke 84V Lithium-Polymer battery pack.

Summertime Water Condensing Unit

A cost efficient water collection concept

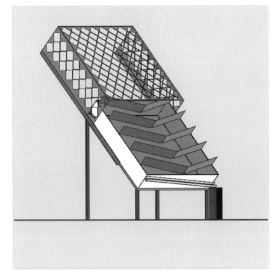 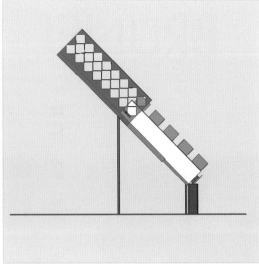

Many hot countries suffer from the absence of water, and yet the amount of dew in the atmosphere can be considerable. Condensation of moisture to dew has been understood for a long time, but due to its low efficiency and the fact that it depends on the unpredictability of the weather, it has not been further developed until recently. Dew ponds were built in ancient Britain to catch the morning dew and similar ideas abound in the Middle East. On a commercial scale, seawater is used to condense air moisture for use in greenhouse, depicted by the projects performed by the Seawater Greenhouse Co Ltd.

In the midst of the global warming phenomenon, energy producing systems will be designed to use non carbon emitting energy sources such as wind, solar or night sky, or combinations of renewable energy resources. OPUR is the leading organisation dealing in research of such systems, and their systems' prices range from € 150 to € 11,000, which depends both on the size and method of cooling.

The aim of the project was to design a small scale water condensing system for the outdoors that will condense moisture from the atmospheric moist air and obtain water for domestic purposes for regions of the South East of England.

Team members researched previous methods used by others to condense moisture from air, and the available cooling methods that could be used to make the condensing unit reach temperatures below the dew point, which would result in moisture being produced. The use of a decision matrix along with critical discussions of the concept models resulted in a rigorous approach to selecting the final design. The selected design uses the principle of a radiative collector to condense moisture at night. This design was optimised via computer simulations. The final product resulted in a system that provides an alternative source of water for people to use during the hosepipe ban season in the South East region of England.

The importance of this investigation has been highlighted by the new water surcharge that will vary the unit cost of water between winter and summer. As per the new regulations, water will now cost 99.9p per litre in the summer, while in winter the rate will drop to 92.2p, emphasising the benefits of purchasing the radiative moisture condenser. At this rate of 99.9 p per litre, and the product producing 3.628 l/night, it amounts to a saving of about 544.2 L corresponding to about £500 over the driest month of the summer (from May to September).

Team Members:

Audley Franklin
Baboo Gowreesunker
Stephen Kago
Vishal Shah

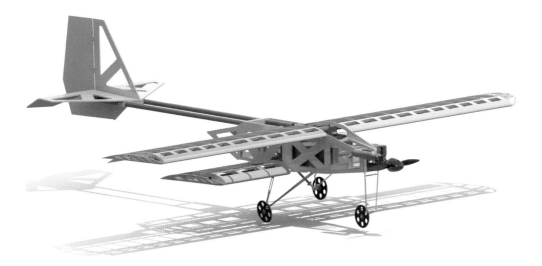

This project involved the design, manufacture, and testing of a model aircraft, suited for competition in the 2010 Heavy Lift Challenge. This takes place every June, run by the British Model Flying Association (BMFA).

In accordance with competition rules, the aircraft was designed entirely by a student group, working within constraints including a known engine and a limited wingspan. The principle aim of this design is to maximize the ratio of payload weight to aircraft weight (the weight of the aircraft when empty).

Design and analysis performed in different branches of aerospace engineering during this project included aerodynamics, structures, control, stability, and propulsion. The final aircraft design proposal is original in its configuration as a sesquiplane, which builds upon previous experience and research, hopefully giving an edge over previous teams and institutions.

The project as a whole has exemplified the complete aircraft design process, using innovative thinking to fulfill the desired product requirements. It has provided an opportunity to build constructive experience of team working skills, a valuable asset to launching careers in the aerospace industry.

Team Members:

Fenella Allery
Peter McQuillan
Patrick Walton
Daniel Bancfoft
Anthony Liu

Helirotor

Installation of a rig for testing scale helicopter rotor blades

Helicopter operation relies upon the rapid spinning of a rotor or rotors, which subsequently causes vibrations throughout the system. It is vital to know and understand how these vibrations will affect the structure and components in the system to prevent any problems or damage. Extensive testing and modeling of the blades and the system is therefore required for the system to be deemed safe for operation, and to be successfully certified to national and international standards. Due to this, research into new methods of modeling helicoptor rotor blades is a continuing task of topical interest.

The Helirotor project primarily consisted of the design and manufacture of a helirotor rig, which is for the purpose of testing one-fifth scale helicoptor rotor blades. The rotor blades tested were based upon the Westland Lynx helicoptor, and the rig as a whole is approximately 800mm long, 660mm wide, and 1570mm tall, with a diameter of 2270mm when the blades are attached.

Before this rig could be used to run experiments, it required installation into Brunel University. This project looked into the operational needs of the rig and from them developed the necessary designs and decisions needed for the installation. This process included the safety considerations involved with the operation of the rig, selection of the rig parts, designing the layout of the rig and safety enclosure, project costing, and computer modeling of the rotor blades.

Team Members:

Andrew Heaton
Manuel Esperon Miguez
Jestine Thomas
Jithin Thomas
Martin Lawrence

humanistic innovation

Products and concepts to improve the lives of people

Humanistic design and engineering thinking is at the heart of creating innovative opportunities to affect people's daily lives for the better on both a global, corporate and personal scale. Humanistic Thinking generates socially aware concepts, brands and strategies that are specifically developed to improve the lives of individuals, whatever their needs.

Tulipe
Feedback plant pot

Age related macular degeneration is a sight condition that affects almost 50% of over 75s in the UK. The condition reduces central vision, sometimes leaving people unable to read or focus on fine detail at all. With so many elderly people spending the majority of their time in the home, keeping an active mind is important. With the loss of central vision it is easy to lose freedom and personal confidence. Tulipe uses horticulture therapy to help sufferers by offering gardening as a potential hobby to improve confidence.

Tulipe is a smart plant pot that tells the user if there is something wrong with the plant through a colour-changing base. This colour change is spread over the entire base and therefore is something that most macular degeneration sufferers will be able to see. There is an added vibration alert for those with lower sight levels. The pot warns the user if the plant is too dry, too hot or too cold and if the surroundings are too light or dark.

Natalie King
Industrial Design BSc

Also on p.315

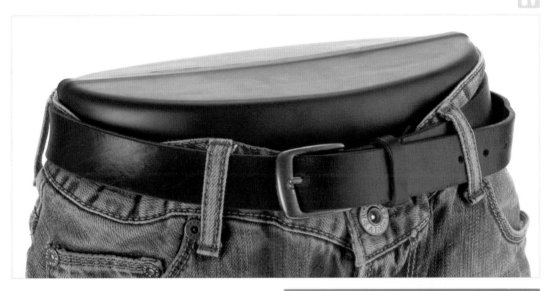

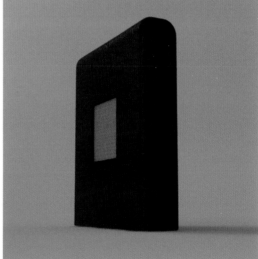

Stealth theft is a major problem throughout Europe, particularly in cities such as Barcelona which contain numerous warning signs about this pervasive form of personal theft. In 2008 there were 725,000 recorded incidents of theft from people in the UK alone. 85% of these were stealth thefts such as pick pocketing. Travellers' behaviour presents many opportunities that thieves exploit: men tend to place their most valuable items in their pockets, where as women tend to place their most valuable items in their handbags.

Currently travellers purchase very few anti-theft devices due to their inherent inconvenience. The brief was therefore set as 'a solution that would massively restrict third party access to valuables without compromising usability for the owner.' The design incorporated the use of a mechanism to block access to the pocket for all 3rd parties with the exception of the user, whose trigger removes all barriers allowing access to their valuables. The design focused on power consumption, ergonomics and overall effectiveness.

Max Borgeat
Product Design BSc

Golf for Kids

Adjustable club which optimises the golfing performance of children

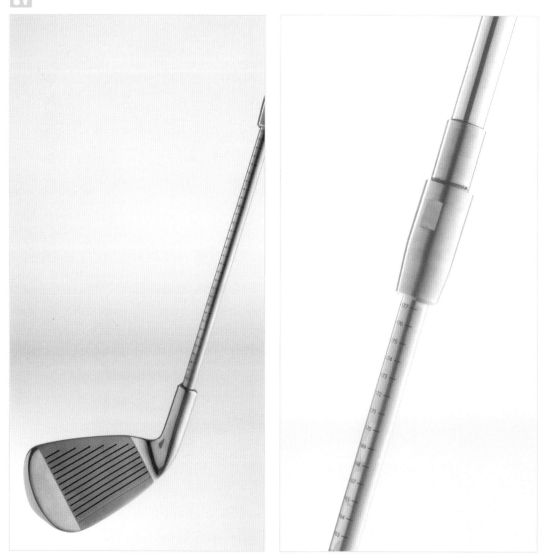

The popularity of golf has been consistently decreasing, particularly among children. As the game is so dependent on ergonomics it should be no surprise that children encounter difficulties using one club size throughout their growth. Small changes in the club length and weight distribution have a large impact on posture, swing path, and inevitably performance. Children using a wrongly sized club struggle to maintain consistency and interest. By maintaining the desired ratio of player height to club length, the adjustable golf club can grow with the child, maintaining the consistency and 'club feel' which is very important to improving their own performance and providing adjustment as they grow and improve their proficiency.

The adjustable golf club offers an economical benefit to the parents of the children, who purchase only 2 sets of golf clubs as their child grows instead of 5 or more. The golf club's maintained balance, centre of gravity and weight ensures continuity throughout the child's growth.

Adrian Bliss

Industrial Design & Technology BA

Also on p.157

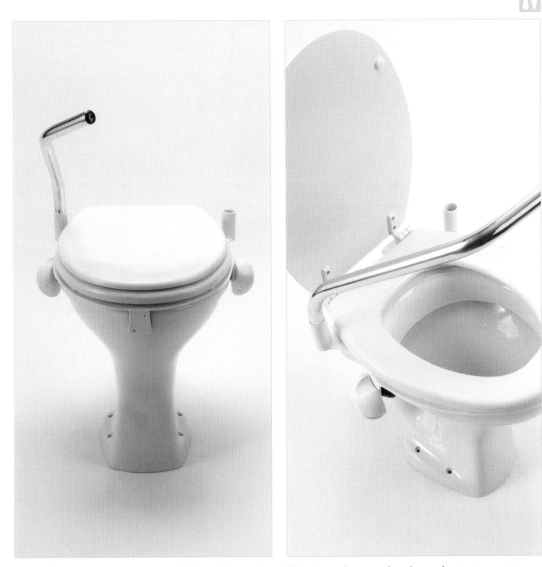

In the UK alone there are 70,000 children who require mobility aids to cope with the Activities of Daily Living (ADL), and many of them have difficulties in independent toileting. The Medical Engineering Resource Unit (MERU) specialises in producing unique equipment and products to support these individuals. This MERU-commissioned project focuses on developing a portable toilet seat adaptation for small batch production.

The clamping mechanism adapts to most pans providing a secure base for attaching a customised support system that comfortably stabilises the user in a relaxed manner. The product alleviates anxieties that make toileting difficult and embarrassing, giving an improved user and carer experience. Its portability allows most toilets to be adapted whilst the user is enjoying other activities, away from their home environment. Toileting need no longer be an issue for people with disabilities.

Ben Boutcher-West
Industrial Design & Technology BA

Also on p.148

Colour Blindness in the Classroom
Helping teachers identify and understand pupils with colour-vision deficiency

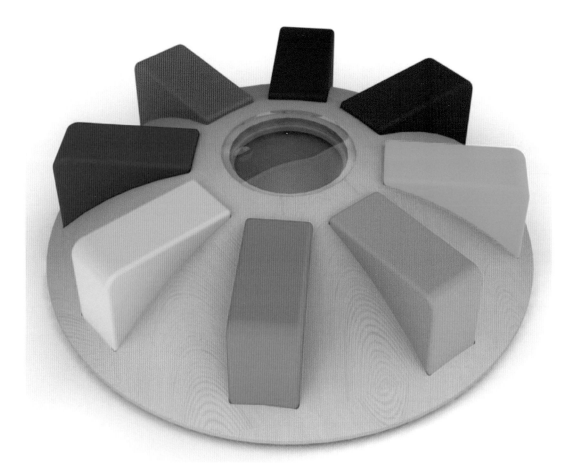

This project is aimed at improving the primary school experience for students who have a colour vision deficiency. The most commonly known red-green colour blindness affects 1 in 20 males. Despite this high prevalence, awareness of colour blindness is very limited. Many people including teachers assume that vision is limited to greyscale.

This mechanical colour-changing tool is designed to provide a quick colour matching exercise. The teacher presses the central button to change the colour displayed, and the pupil selects the colour block that looks closest in colour to them. The design deliberately discourages scoring or grading of the pupil, but allows the teacher to actively observe any mismatches. This is not a medical diagnostic device, but an indicator to raise the teacher's awareness of potential colour vision defects among the students. The simplicity of the activity minimizes the time that a pupil is removed from the class, and offers maximum learning for the teacher in those few minutes.

Yvonne Dalton
Product Design Engineering BSc

These music blocks make use of an alphabet block form to enhance and encourage musical creativity and to help in the understanding of musical theory from a young age. Each block individually sounds a single note, and when joined to another block plays in tandem to create simple chords. Multiple blocks aligned together can be triggered to create a sequential tune. Taking on the wooden form of traditional instruments and toys introduces children to the feel and texture of the musical medium, whilst giving individual notes a physical form, and tangible nature, to assist the learning of audio, visual, spatial, or kinaesthetic relations.

The blocks are manufactured to be durable and are not only useful for the young but also as a learning aid for older first time learners, or even as a novelty item for the musically minded. They are intended to be high quality batch items, with a low ecological footprint and high environmental awareness.

Mia Foo
Product Design BSc

PlayPal

Engaging parental involvement in early childhood development

Children's quality of play is highly influential during preschool development. However with the rise in working households and passive entertainment, busy parents can find themselves lacking the time to provide this.

PlayPal encourages social and emotional development by promoting parent and child interaction, rather than replacing it. Reducing barriers to capturing spontaneous activities, PlayPal enables families to visualise their time spent together.

Whether it's making cakes after work, or playing with a cardboard box, PlayPal provides a 'Show and Tell' medium for parent and child to reflect on and inspire.

By fixing the bendable camera to any surface, both parent and child are photographed as they play. Taken at selected time intervals, these natural photos catch unseen moments. While the PIR sensor and embedded software ensure the frame motivates parents and children to want to play together.

Ross Dudley

Industrial Design & Technology BA

Also on p.306

Crossed Wires

A social skills teaching aid for young people with ASD

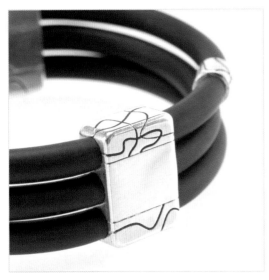

Autistic Spectrum Disorders affect 1 in every 100 people in the UK and people with ASD generally struggle with social skills. Currently there is a lack of support for young people with ASD as they move towards university and the wider world. Crossed Wires is an innovative concept to help fill this gap. The user selects up to three social skills to improve at a time, tailoring the system to their needs. Each skill is assigned a button on the Crossed Wires bracelet, which the user can discreetly activate whenever a problem in this area occurs. This records the time of the event, allowing them to relax and enjoy their day knowing they can address the problem later on.

To do so, they connect the bracelet to their computer, via the USB concealed in the clasp. This displays when the buttons have been activated, indicating which skill requires attention. The user can then undertake a carefully designed social skills training programme, to help them understand the problem that occurred and learn to reduce the chance of it reoccurring.

Stephanie Fox

Industrial Design & Technology BA

Also on p.247

About 50% of Camden residents do not use a car, so they rely heavily on public transport, walking and cycling. Older people form a significant part of this group, reflecting the increasing number of older people in the UK. They are also more likely to make shorter trips due to lack of mobility or other impairments. The "Safety Indicator Accessory" is a device that increases the visibility of the cyclist to other road users, with the intent of increasing confidence, full control and security.

The product establishes wireless communication between the discrete control box attached to the belt, and the buttons on the handlebars. When a button is pressed to signal a change in direction, LEDs on the belt flash to clearly indicate this to other road users, and to increase the cyclist's visibility on the road.

Victoria Grantham
Industrial Design & Technolgy BA

Also on p.138

Flat-Pack Malaria Prevention Cot for Cambodia

Reducing child mortality rates from malaria

Malaria causes the deaths of over 3000 children every day around the world, especially infants under five. Many children experience up to six episodes of malaria each year, all of them potentially fatal.

In association with The World Medical Fund for Children, Help the Cambodian Children Charity and support from the Innovation Team at UNICEF the cot has been designed for use in Cambodia, where malaria related mortalities rose by more than 58% in the first half of 2009 alone.

Mosquito nets can entangle babies, tear easily, and be hung incorrectly. This double skin, flat-packed cot has been designed to avoid these pitfalls and solve bed-sharing problems, including overcrowding, entrapment and humidity. It provides a comfortable, sustainable, safe and individual space for the most vulnerable children.

Christopher Harkin

Industrial Design & Technology BA

Also on p.246

Bicycle theft is a huge problem across the UK, with one bicycle stolen every minute. In the context of climate change and rising obesity the government is keen to get commuters cycling on a regular basis. Overcoming the fear and reality of bicycle theft is a crucial barrier to overcome before this can be achieved.

Many existing locks are bought separately as a security measure to secure a bicycle to an immovable object, but have largely proven ineffective and easily neutralised. RotaLock is an addition to the bicycle design that immobilizes the bicycle as well as preventing theft of the wheel. This stops the possibility of theft without causing crucial damage to the bicycle, making RotaLock an effective step towards inherently secure bicycle design.

The locking mechanism has been specially designed to allow for easy locking by the user and can be factory fitted to as many existing bicycle forks as possible.

Karl Jolly
Product Design BSc

Enhancing the Daily Life of a Wheelchair User

Assisting independent transfer

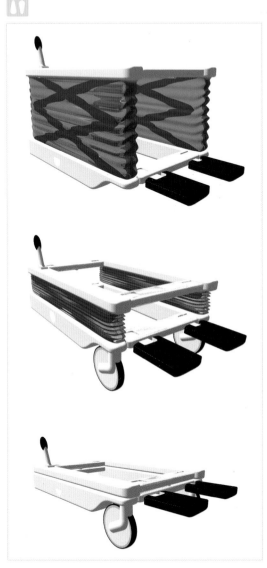

The project was focused on understanding the needs and aspirations of less confident and less experienced manual wheelchair users, seeking to enhance their daily life by identifying and eliminating barriers to performing everyday activities independently.

A poor wheelchair design creates barriers to performing a given task. This results in the need to develop techniques and assistive products which cope with these barriers. Wheelchair design should give users less to compete with not more! Standardised wheelchair design has a very important impact on user transfer (the movement from one surface to another), a core daily activity. The project brief was to design and development a standardised wheelchair frame which enhanced the user's ability to manually perform independent user transfers to and from a range of surface heights without impacting the implicit advantages of standardised chair design.

Michael Jones

Industrial Design & Technology BA

Also on p.307

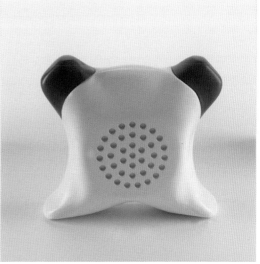

AFFA is an inclusively designed alarm to rouse people who are deaf or hard of hearing from their sleep in the event of a fire. It takes into account people's specific hearing capabilities by allowing the alarm frequency to be adjusted to whatever is most appropriate.

This RNID-supported project targets the needs of over 9 million people in the UK. Optional strobe lighting and vibrating pad attachments ensure that the alarm will not go unnoticed. AFFA uses a wireless system to monitor the other AFFA units around it, and when any

AFFA is triggered, all of them will sound. This reduces response time, which is critical in an emergency, and gives people a more secure and comfortable night's sleep.

Freddie Jordan
Industrial Design & Technology BA

Also on p.321

Designer Councils
Improving the strategic use of design

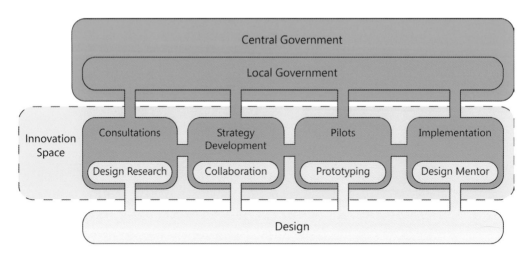

The Local Government supplies many services that the public interact with on a daily basis. Design is recognised as an effective way to innovate within the public services, however its adoption as a strategic tool is scarce and scattered.

Through an evaluation of current Local Government, the project established the contexts in which design is being implemented. The situations where strategic design was achieved were critiqued, leading to an understanding of how and why design can be constructive. Observational research at a Local Council and at a service innovation consultancy, alongside interviews and experimental design validation methods, refined and lent evidence to design's value in specific situations. The final recommendations included creation of the above simplified supporting framework, identifying areas of strategic design use.

The framework shows how design currently operates within other practices and systems. It is adopted on a project-by-project basis and functions as a total process. The study found that to increase strategic design's use, it must function alongside existing working practices. This will enhance and enrich the current processes rather than replace them. The enchanced adoption of design methods and processes are recommended in the following key areas.

Consultation
Design research methods should be embedded into traditional consultation strategies. Design research tools such as observational methods would become available as forms of consultation. Residents would be involved at every stage.

Strategy development
Design processes should be embedded into current strategic development methods. Collaborative design processes and tools such as co-design and design workshops would improve joined up thinking and creativity.

Service Pilot
The prototyping of service concepts should become continuous and active before the pilot/trial stage, to better validate and work through concepts.

Implementation
The design field usually has a point reference, a client who is liased with throughout the process. A design process practitioner would help navigate the implementation. That would ensure that all requirements are met and that direction is not diluted from the transfer between theory and practice. Being responsible for the process the design pracitioner would also help to ensure accountability for the design implementation.

Tobi Lawal
Mechanical Engineering & Design MEng

Also on p.308

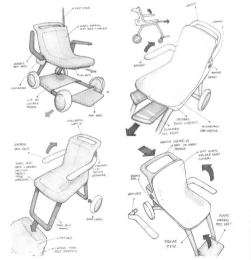

Potentially lethal hospital associated infections are costing the NHS £4000 to £10,000 per patient, equating to £1 billion per year.

Transport chairs pose particular infection risks as they travel throughout the hospital and are used by staff, visitors, and patients. Often transport chairs are difficult to clean and are not included in a cleaning rota, making them ideal places for infections to harbour and spread.

The primary function of this design is its ease of cleaning, yet it also aims to increase user awareness of hygiene within hospitals, and make patients feel more dignified. This chair has a reduced number of points which multiple users will touch, increasing cleanability and minimizing opportunities for infection to be transferred to the chair.

The chair uses a clean aesthetic to remind staff of its need for cleaning on a daily basis, helping to control the risk of hospital related infections.

Francis Lofthouse
Industrial Design BSc

Also on p.130

Spedz

An interactive and unique approach targeting childhood obesity

Obesity is an increasingly important issue in the western world, with 25 percent of boys and 33 percent of girls aged 2 to 19 years classed as overweight or obese. Multiple solutions were considered, with the fitness and physical activity route identified as an area for improvement. This pedometer is designed especially for children, focusing on interface design for children to provide clear informative feedback on their daily walking and running regime.

Utilising and understanding of child psychology

resulted in a product that is engaging for 7 to 10 year olds. The hardware interfaces with a PC via USB, where the software aspect tracks cumulative progress, allowing children to compare their activity levels against each other, parents and teachers.

At first, extrinsic motivation is fostered to encourage exercise, which develops into intrinsic motivation with use. The pedometer is inclusive to all able bodied children regardless of physical fitness. It adapts targets based on the child's past daily progress.

Peter McClelland
Industrial Design BSc

Also on p.245

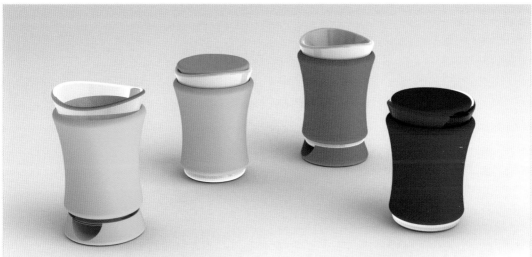

Every year, it is estimated that 150,000 people have a stroke in the UK, and in the UK alone there are over 300,000 people living with moderate to severe disabilities as a result of a stroke.

When the demands of using a product surpass the capabilities of the intended user, design exclusion occurs. Existing products have some degree of design exclusion and the majority of the currently available drinking aids stigmatise the user, lowering their sense of personal dignity.

Malcolm Johnston once stated that "Peoples' attitudes towards their disability and their self-image are directly affected by their equipment". Hug counters design exclusion by providing the user an inclusive product which holds no negative stigma and which allows people to keep their independence and build self confidence, improving their personal dignity.

Also on p.64

Nick Pettett
Industrial Design & Technology BA

FireFly

Inclusive fire alarm design

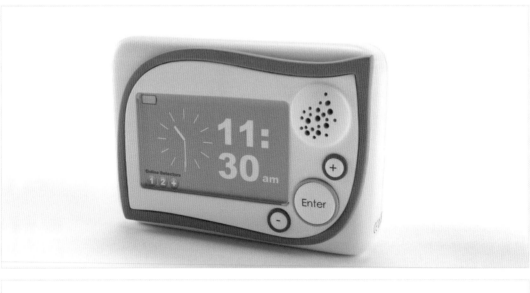

FireFly is multi-sensory fire alarm system which uses existing wireless smoke alarm technology. The product consists of a large-screen fire alarm system that monitors all smoke detectors in the house, wirelessly. FireFly then relays the information back to the user in an easily understandable visual way. FireFly is designed for people who suffer from mild to moderate hearing loss. The product includes a variable frequency alarm and a clear visual warning, and communicates with your mobile phone which then acts as a tactile alert. FireFly has been designed not as an assistive product, but as an inclusive device. It aims to remove the preconceptions and stigmas associated with assistive design. It addresses a need for change in user behaviour with regards to fire alarms, and increases the effectiveness of the alarm.

This project was supported by RNID and is being evaluated for further development towards commercialisation.

Tom Etheridge

Industrial Design & Technology BA

Also on p.310

Love Your Hands
Dermatitis prevention unit with disposable glove donning aid

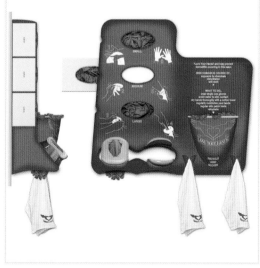

Up to 70% of hairdressers suffer from work-related skin damage at some point. Love Your Hands is a user-centred desirable system to improve disposable glove donning, aiming to prevent Occupational Contact Dermatitis (OCD) occurring amongst apprentice hairdressers whilst at work. OCD can be avoided by eliminating contact with wet and harmful substances. User research into single-use gloves highlighted donning and removal as an issue. By making this safer and more desirable the project encourages disposable glove use in salons. A simple,

appropriate graphical element within the product educates users by explaining the dangers of OCD and the importance of wearing gloves.

An innovative feature of Love Your Hands is a system that allows the disposal of single-use gloves into a contained area. This avoids contamination and aids efficient glove recycling, helping to reduce the carbon footprint of the salon.

Also on p.60

Amy Godsell
Industrial Design BSc

Service Plus
Restaurant plate waiting aid

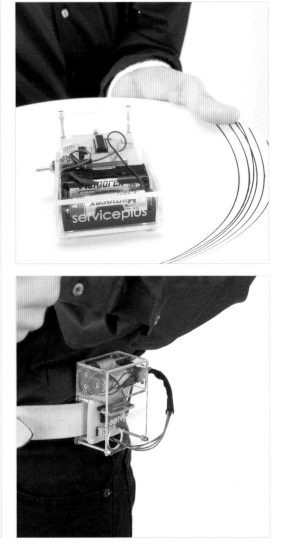

Service Plus detects the instability of plates, trays or other hand-held items that waiters and waitresses often carry as part of their daily work. It then makes use of vibro-tactile stimulation to inform them of any precariously balanced items. The product is designed to assist the existing proprioceptory systems which are used when the waiter or waitress' attention is focused upon other duties.

The proven technological principles of this innovative product have a broader market potential than the restaurant-based user group at the centre of this preliminary study.

James Gunton
Industrial Design & Technology BA

Also on p.155

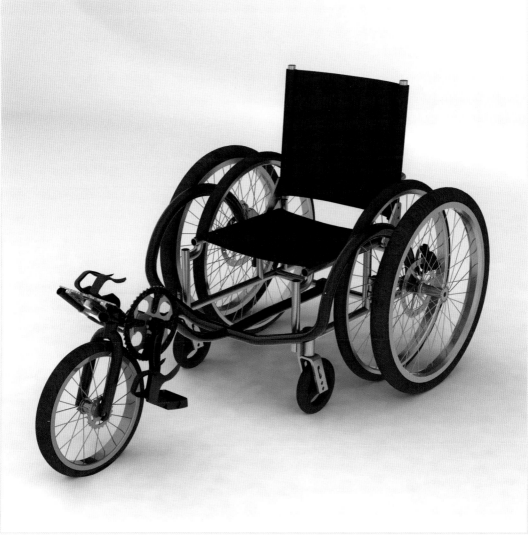

This project involved working with a client who suffers from Cerebral Palsy, who desired the increased capability to ride a bicycle, such that he could benefit from the freedom of transporting himself, while also taking advantage of the physical exercise.

Chariot is a bespoke bicycle designed specifically for the client, though there are also many people with similar requirements who would benefit from the inclusive operational elements incorporated within the tricycle design. The tricycle is fully leg-operated

and incorporates innovative use of existing cycling elements, which facilitate operation with the lower body alone. Chariot is designed to connect with existing wheelchairs and is propelled by a simple rotary pedalling arrangement. It uses innovative operational systems such as skid steering, which utilises braking to provide two cycling functions.

The final concept design takes account of the physical limitations of body function imposed by Cerebral Palsy, which were all tested to ensure definitive concept feasibility.

Nick Harrod
Industrial Design & Technology BA

Also on p.309

Drinkup

A simple and effective solution to encourage water consumption in the elderly population

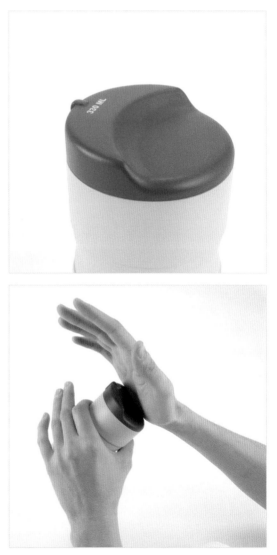

Keeping hydrated is a crucial process in human life, yet so much of the population fails to maintain a healthy level of hydration. In 2008, dehydrated patients took up more than 70,000 hospital bed days, and the majority of these people were over 65. This is largely due to the products on the market being unsuitable for older people. Many of the drinking bottles marketed as "easy to use" feature heavily on 'ergonomic' designs that are not intuitive to many users.

Using subtle ergonomics, and taking emotional and functional design into consideration, Drinkup is a reusable bottle that encourages older people to drink more water. Its reduced dimensions and focus on ease of use, promotes an inherent behaviour change with regards to hydration. Aesthetics and quality of material also play a large role in the design, aiming to instill a sense of pride and ownership to a product that is often seen as cheap and disposable.

Bradly Hood
Industrial Design & Technology BA

Also on p.160

In the context of an ageing population, and higher diagnosis of disability, many more people are passing through at least one stage in their lives when they will use medication on a daily basis.

Neurological conditions such as Alzheimer's disease can cause memory loss and make older people particularly reliant on their family and carers in their day-to-day living activities. Although Alzheimer's is incurable, its symptoms can sometimes be reduced by carefully administered medication. This can lead to a complex pill regime requiring a carer to be present to ensure that the user is taking the right dosage at the right time. This electronic pill dispenser prompts the user to take pills at the correct time of day by means of a recording of a familiar voice. The user is able to manage their medication independently without risk, and the workload of the carer is eased.

Michael Matey
Industrial Design BSc

Also on p.57

BaseDry
A hair dryer for people suffering from arthritis

9 million people in the UK suffer from osteoarthritis or rheumatoid arthritis, and 70% of these are female. The hair drying process currently requires strenuous and awkward movements when a standard hair dryer is used. Although assistive hair dryers are available, they are usually limited by being fixed to a wall or surface, and can be stigmatising for the user.

BaseDry makes use of inclusive design principles to make hair drying easier and less demanding for all users, particularly those with arthritis. BaseDry enhances the independence and self-image of women with arthritis whilst its simple, approachable aesthetic also makes it appealing to all of us. The portable mains-rechargeable base unit can be placed on a convenient flat surface, and the light hose attachment unreels to assist easy hair drying without demanding high levels of upper body mobility. The hose attachment is ergonomically designed to provide a comfortable grip, and the product rewinds to be compact, easy to carry and store.

John New
Industrial Design BSc

Also on p.235

FRESH is an innovative new method for teaching young people how to cook meals for themselves using only fresh unprocessed ingredients. It is targeted at the thousands of young students who start their first year at university not knowing how to cook healthy meals.

The recipe is presented in an innovative new style containing pictorial instructions such that it is easy for the user to quickly see exactly how to prepare the meal. This visual method also makes it easy for them to memorise recipes. Every recipe is designed to take 20 minutes or less to prepare and cook.

All of the ingredients needed to cook the meal are contained inside the box in their raw state, and in the correct proportions. This minimises the amount of food waste created, and encourages users to eat well-balanced healthily sized portions.

Tom Pilgrim
BSc Product Design

Also on p.114

Next Stop: 2025
An inclusive bus wayfinding solution

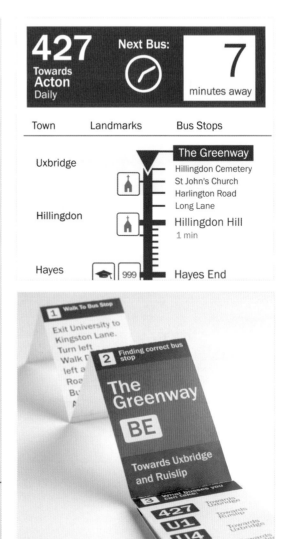

With more than 30% of the UK population expected to be over 55 years old by 2025, the needs of Britain's older population are of increasing concern. In London, anyone over 60 is eligible for free public transport, however government statistics show that 45% of people over 75 struggle with using the bus.

This future concept for a bus stop, developed in collaboration with fwdesign, focuses on a more inclusive society and on improving the bus transport experience for everyone, including older individuals.

Incorporating TFL's new iBus and GPS tracking system, Next Stop offers digital information to passengers at standing flag stops through live information boards and flag signs, replacing the existing printed timetables. This new information system is complemented by three designs for physical structures that provide increased shelter compared to current flag stops. The whole system is brought together with personalised Journey Cards containing step-by-step directions guiding the user's travel from their front door to their final destination.

Francisco Rebello
Industrial Design & Technology BA

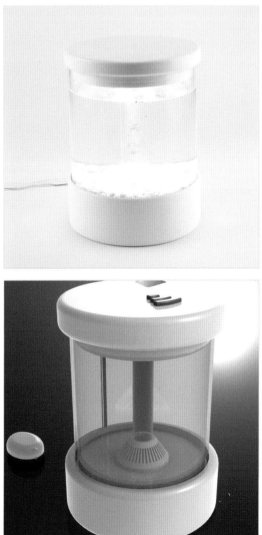

Stress relief is a mood light that makes use of the psychological benefits of viewing nature and living organisms. The natural viewing is combined with a day/night lighting cycle, which influences human circadian rhythms, to help regulate a user's work and sleep cycles through the day. The aquatic creatures and plants contained within create relaxing visuals as they swim, casting interesting shadows and movement when combined with the lighting and water. This results in a relaxing, stress reducing user experience.

This product innovates through the depth of psychological research undertaken during its development, and by means of the scientific principles which it is based upon. Today many mood lights are gimmicks or novelty items, with limited use as truly effective stress relief devices. By contrast, this light incorporates a self-contained natural ecosystem which appeals to the human subconscious biophilia, providing a focal source that can reduce work fatigue through its natural stimuli.

Jaymes Schular
Industrial Design & Technology BA

Also on p.229

Rapid Deployment Eco Hospital
Modular, low impact, human centred building system

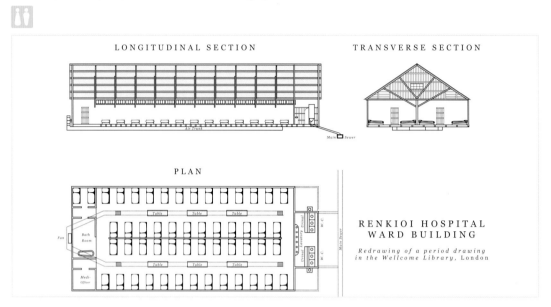

LONGITUDINAL SECTION

TRANSVERSE SECTION

PLAN

RENKIOI HOSPITAL
WARD BUILDING

*Redrawing of a period drawing
in the Wellcome Library, London*

Designed for the Crimean War (1853-1856). From April 1854 to June 1856 only 10% of the 18,000 war casualties were caused by battlefield injuries, the remaining deaths being from illness such as cholera, diarrhoea and typhoid as a result of overcrowded and insanitary hospitals. This was the war in which Florence Nightingale and Mary Seacole made their names through their nursing work and political pressure for healthcare reform, although Nightingale's book Notes on Hospitals was not published until 4 years after the hospital was built. Hospital space was urgently needed. A modular design was created which could be prefabricated and delivered to a chosen site as a complete package, including all ventilation and sewage components for each 50 bed, 100ft x 40ft x 25ft, module. Total plans were for 60 ward modules with a capacity for 3000 patients.

The timescale from briefing to the admission of the first patients was only nine months, from February to October 1855. A complete prototype was built one month after briefing. The innovations were numerous: Inspiration for modular building was drawn from Paxton's Great Exhibition built four years earlier. Each component of the predominantly timber construction was optimised for material utilisation, weight and cost, with no part larger than what could be carried by two men. Plumbing and Sewage was supplied pre-packaged for each unit in case any problems were encountered with the shipment of individual wards, and all modules could all be assembled using dry joints. The design incorporated

mechanically assisted ventilation, flushing toilets (only 3 years after the introduction of the Jennings siphon water closet) and plumbed-in wash basins. Environmental control was further enhanced with a tin roof covering to reflect sun in the high summer temperatures, and provision for insulation to be added from the inside during winter. The Hospital planning, supply, installation, operation and re-use were all considered and design-managed by Brunel. For example, a rail track took incoming patients the short distance from the specially build quay to the hospital buildings so as to minimise transportation times for badly injured patients. During it's operation the hospital had a death rate of 3.75% compared to 12.65% at the other Crimean hospitals.

Isambard Kingdom Brunel
Fellow of the Royal Society

Pulse is an interactive auditory activity aimed at helping children through the transition to wearing a hearing aid. For a child being fitted for a hearing aid for the first time, the process can be confusing, intrusive and troubling. Depending on the individual, the worst cases can see a refusal to adapt or even wear the aid. Pulse helps ease this problem by providing a platform on which the entire family can play games and interact with sound. By providing the child with a replica hearing aid, they have a chance to become familiar with the aid and understand its benefits.

The product consists of four replica hearing aids, along with the conical device used to play the games. The concept involves the use of audio induction loop technology, with the replicas being the receiver and the conical device the transmitter. The activities can be changed and involve challenges that range from memory games, through to sound recording.

By providing a fun and engaging introduction to hearing aids, Pulse makes life easier and more comfortable for the child and their family.

Simon Smith
Industrial Design BSc

Also on p.314

Transitions
Unique movement-based musical instrument for wheelchair users

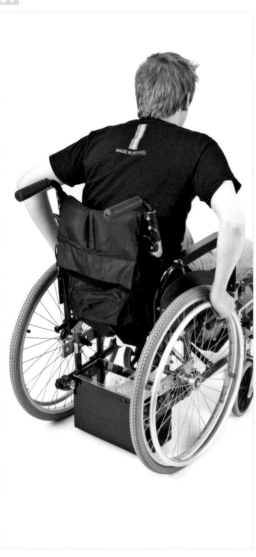

There are thousands of different musical instruments, yet few that are designed with wheelchair users in mind. Transitions has been developed in collaboration with Joy of Sound and MERU as a musical instrument for music therapy and therapeutic group sessions for adults with various disabilities, who use manual wheelchairs.

Transitions is an electronic musical instrument that attaches to the undercarriage of an adult manual wheelchair. It receives input either from manual propulsion of the wheelchair, or from a D9 joystick input. This is then converted into sound, based on the direction changes. Transitions encourages the use of everyday movements to create music, and is therefore a far more accessible instrument to those with limited mobility.

The product was developed as a one-off for Joy Of Sound, but with further development it could be batch manufactured for other music therapy groups, and for schools.

Annabelle Spender
Industrial Design & Technology BA

Also on p.234

littlepal
Stress reducing medical device for children's healthcare visits

littlepal reduces stress during children's injections through the use of visual, tactile and sonic distraction. It consists of a specialized tray and syringe shrouds styled in the form of animal characters. The use of play and toy-like characterisation adds a feeling of familiarity and the choice of characters gives the child a sense of control in an often traumatic experience.

littlepal is designed to make the adult user hold the syringe in a certain way, minimizing the likelihood of improper insertion or injury. The medical tray is two-shot moulded plastic, which creates an appealing colour break, and mutes unwanted noise from equipment moving around the tray. The packaging itself contains a comic-like narrative of the character, which enables the child to imaginatively understand their treatment, tackling their fear of the unknown.

The key aspect of this product is the shrouding of the needle, which helps reduce anticipatory anxiety, resulting in a more relaxed and pleasurable experience.

Terry Stokes
Industrial Design BSc

Also on p.220

Foot massager

For prevention of plantar fasciitis and related injuries.

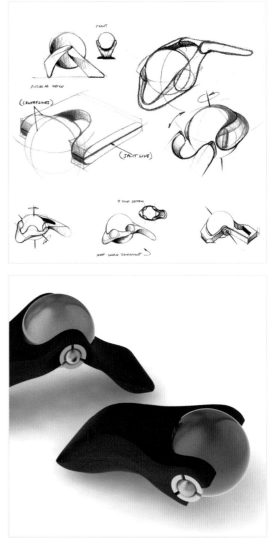

Most people over 30 have experienced heel pain at some point in their lives, but are likely to ignore it. Around 15% of the adult population have symptoms of plantar fasciitis, swelling of the connective tissue on the base of the foot. When ignored, plantar fasciitis can develop into more serious issues of the ankles, knees, hips or back.

This foot massager addresses the importance of a responsible approach towards heel pain. Market research, user requirement research, and ongoing feedback were used to develop an aesthetically pleasing and functionally sound design. The resulting product is aimed at an inclusive market, and is particularly optimized for use by athletes. It can also be used inclusively within the home, work or hospital environment to relieve all types of heel pain.

Anton Khmelev

Industrial Design & Technology BA

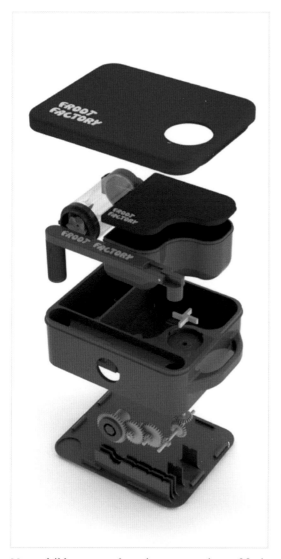

Many children are only eating two portions of fruit and vegetables a day. As an average child's lunchbox accounts for a third of their daily food intake. Lunchtime is a great opportunity to encourage children to improve their eating behaviour. The Froot Factory, designed to appeal to children 6 to 12 years old, helps to increase children's fruit consumption whilst at school. The Froot Factory lunchbox incorporates a hand-powered smoothie maker, allowing children to get involved in the preparation of their food and be excited at the prospect of eating their own fruity concoctions. The Froot Factory's integrated design enables children to lead the creation of their fruit smoothie from beginning to end.

Anil Toora
Industrial Design & Technology BA

FLOC

For the Love Of Colour

FLOC
perform | create

"FLOC is a response to our daily state of being; a state that is so distinctly out of balance with the environment in which we find ourselves and the operating parameters of the human body we inhabit."

As humans, what we do is largely not natural to our state of human physiology. A typical scenario: every working day of our lives we 'use computers'. We stare at inanimate assemblies of plastics, metals and electronics.

We are invariably stressed and are often under pressure, performing tasks that push us to our limits, and at the end of the working day, we leave this workstation, go home, maybe stare at another collection of electronics for a couple of hours, then go

to bed. The next day we do the same, and probably the day after that too. This behaviour pattern has become a routine that we accept without criticism… it is an odd routine.FLOC is a design concept which has led to the development of two products with commercial potential, having the ability to solve problems caused by this unnatural techno-paradise we live in and enjoy, but ultimately were not designed for.

Fred Ryder
Product Design Engineering BSc

An integral part of a new parent's routine is the washing and drying their new born baby, a processwhich has remained largely unchanged for generations. They have to dry their infant quickly to prevent too much heat being lost, but need to also ensure that all the water is fully removed so as to prevent skin rashes.

This design proposal is a drying table that will assist in the drying process of the baby. It uses gentle streams of warm air along with microfiber materials to increase the efficiency of the drying process. It uses toy flowers with built in fans to re-direct the air blown from the main heater unit, which is located on the wall. The flowers light up when in use and can be pulled, twisted, stretched and compressed in any direction, allowing the parent to position each one as required. When not in use, the flowers retract into the unit making it suitable for storage. The colours, patterns and materials of the flowers also provide a high level of interaction with the baby, thus assisting in the infant's development.

Richard Braine
Product Design BSc

Also on p.107

Sensory Class

Helping teachers plan inclusive multisensory lessons

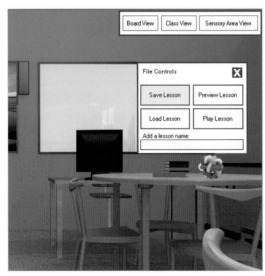

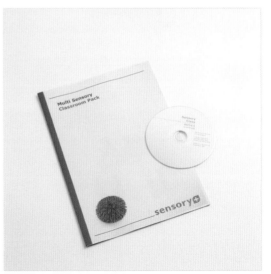

Classes in mainstream Primary schools increasingly include both students with and without Special Educational Needs. More than ever before, teachers are rising to the challenge of providing lessons which include and value every student in their classes.

This project found inspiration in the use of multi-sensory resources in Special Schools, applying core principles such as learning styles to teaching in mainstream classrooms. Sensory Class suite aims to bring multi-sensory teaching and learning to the mainstream by allowing teachers to control all of the electronic multi-sensory resources in their room; including the board, audio, lighting, aroma and much more. Sensory Class focuses on providing a simple sensory toolset that pupils and teachers can use to add excitement to lessons. For example, a fiery theme could be used to explore the Sun, volcanoes or the Great Fire of London. Sensory Class can configure a classroom as a personal quiet room for some SEN students (a feature many schools lack), supporting their transition into mainstream teaching.

Eleanor Rogers

Product Design Engineering BSc

Also on p.116

Future Concepts For Crayola

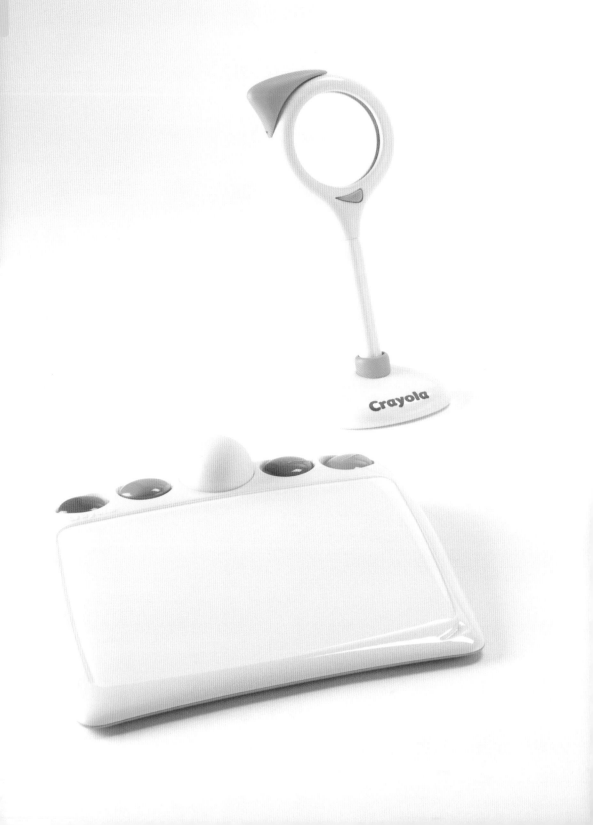

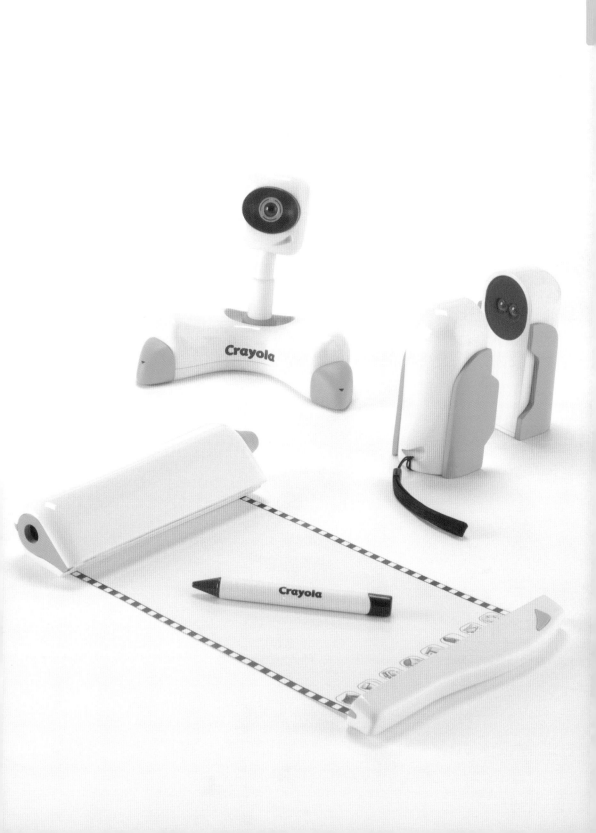

Sensio
Future design concepts for Crayola

Crayola Sensio allows children to engage with messy physical creativity in a clean way. The product harnesses and develops creative motor skills which are often forgotten within the classroom environment.

The product uses a chunky, child-friendly pen which has interchangeable tops, allowing experimentation with brush strokes. The pen is used with a screen tablet which acts as a central hub for the pen and nibs. Crayola Sensio uses haptic feedback and pressure sensors within the pen helping to develop a child's pen holding and physical creativity skills. If the pen is held very hard, the colour will change to mimic their 'hard mood.' This will allow the child to explore different ways of holding and moving the pen across the page.

Sensio allows the child to use their hands and other sensual methods to create colour within their art work. Sensio helps children develop their creativity through haptics and graphical user interfaces with the power of touch and speech reflecting ideas their mood.

Terry Stokes
Industrial Design BSc

Also on p.211

See-Saw is an interactive sketchbook for young children. It is a companion that children can take everywhere they go, recording and sharing what they see and experience, making Crayola creativity truly portable. See-Saw uses cameras to project a digital canvas onto any surface, giving children the freedom they crave to express their creativity. Children create on this canvas using a stylus that keeps the form of the traditional Crayola Crayon, staying true to Crayola's arts and crafts roots.

See-Saw has a user friendly interface based around touch and gestural actions, keeping the Crayola experience relevant to the children of 2025. To e-mail a sketch, the child simply "folds" the projected image and writes the address onto the back of it. This uses technology in the Crayola way to help children to express and share their creativity in a natural and human manner.

Tom Williams
Industrial Design BSc

Also on p.36

Oris
Future design concepts for Crayola

Oris is a little friend that's always there to keep an eye on children's creative development. Through the use of unobtrusive technology, Oris encourages young artists to engage with traditional, tactile media to express themselves.

Extending the neck and pointing the head at the page, Oris sees and records activity as it happens, capturing precious memories and keeping them safe.

Oris publishes the captured creations across a variety of media allowing Mummy, Daddy, friends and family to fully appreciate developing masterpieces.

This design concept aims to maintain the tradition of the Crayola brand by keeping the good old fashioned wax crayons whilst launching Crayola into the future, allowing children to "share their potential".

Ben Davey
Industrial Design BSc

Also on p.92

Spectrum
Future design concepts for Crayola

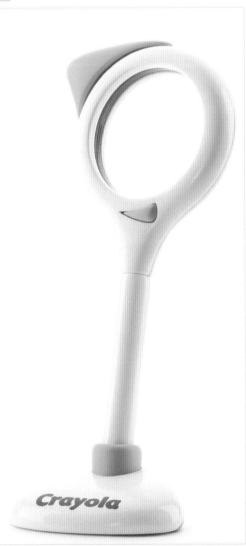

Spectrum allows children the freedom to explore and play with "real" colour. Using HD camera lens technology, photo-realistic colour matching and ink mixing technology, allows children to access an infinite palette of personalised colours.

By aiming Spectrum at a specific colour and pressing on the smile, the child can digitially store and match a "real world" colour swatch. The swatch is then translated into an RGB mix that is used to accurately produce the desired coloured ink. Colour swatches are stored inside Spectrum's memory and can be recalled using the trigger cycle system on the top of Spectrum's head. Spectrum comes with a chargeable docking station which inductively charges the unit for use.

Spectrum will launch the Crayola brand into the future by providing access to sophisticated digital technology for children without compromising Crayola's traditional "Arts and Crafts" heritage. Spectrum actively engages children through "exploratory play" to build on their creative potential.

Joe–Simon Wood
Industrial Design & Technology BA

Also on p.37

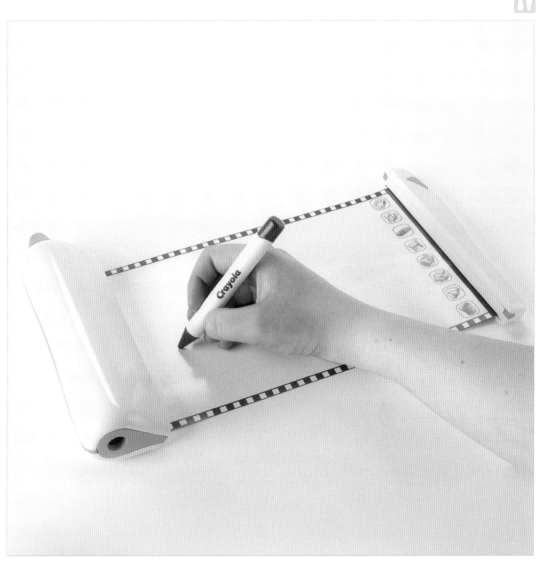

In a world where children are growing older younger and where new technologies advance further into our lives, we could soon loose the physical instructiveness of doing things manually and become lost in a digital world.

Crayola is all about being playful and assisting creativity, interaction and exploration. The brand is innocent; it encourages togetherness with an element of trust between the three stakeholders, the child, the parent and the teacher.

By incorporating these aspects of the brand and brand values with leading edge technology, we glimpse the future.

Scrollie is an interactive scroll that incorporates an educational aspect by teaching the child how to write. Scrollie allows the child to be creative by combining the feel of wax crayon, pen and paper, with a way of selecting colours by twisting the top of the crayon.

Also on p.20

Kishan Mistry
Industrial Design BSc

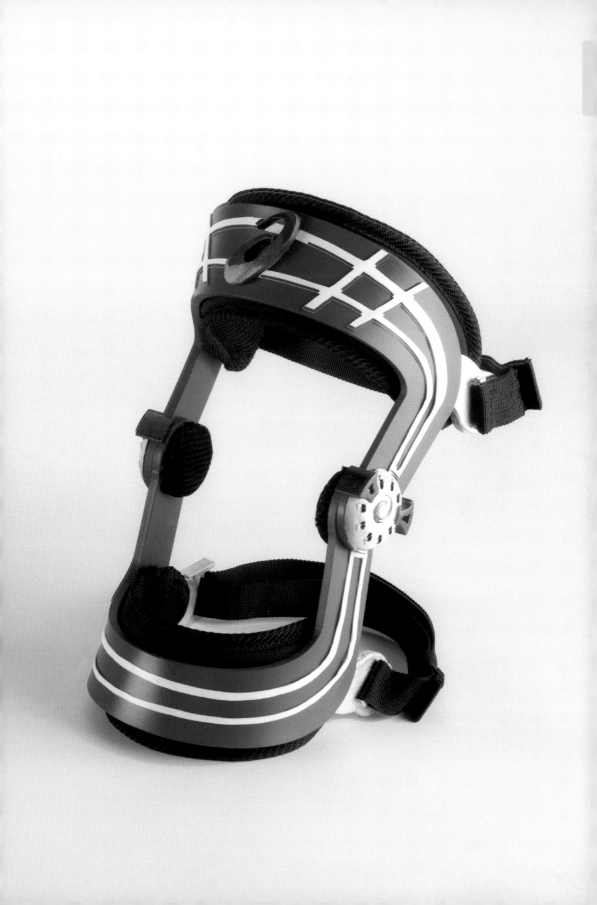

Juggling Balls
Future design concepts for ASICS

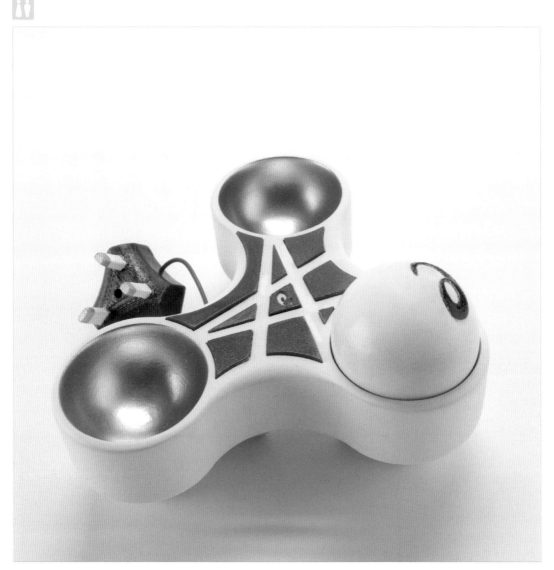

People with Parkinson's Syndrome suffer from dopamine deficiency, where the neurological receptors do not absorb as much dopamine as expected, reducing motor-skills and causing the body to tremble.

The ASICS Juggling Balls are designed to raise the dopamine levels in the brain, increasing the fine motor control skills, which are one of the main issues with the syndrome. The product also improves eye perception and eye hand coordination, raising the quality of life. Increased levels of dopamine also raise pleasure, cognition, memory and learning.

ASICS juggling balls comes with a neat dock charger where the balls can be charged after being used within a virtual world in a game console. Combining the virtual world with reality creates a safer environment for the user. The Juggling Balls are surrounded by ASICS gel technology to protect sensitive electronic components. Moreover, the juggling balls have several more benefits including additional increased motivation levels, happiness and reduced depression.

Azad Saleh
Industrial Design & Technology BA

By studying the ASICS brand two key principles were discovered, the use of new high-tech materials and technology, and depth of understanding of biomechanics. The chosen concept was a knee brace, which incorporated modern materials and technology with ergonomics and human factors within its design. The Knee Brace allows the freedom for older people to get outside and fulfill their aspirations, without being hindered by knee and joint pain. Inspiring confidence through it's design, it will incorporate the ASICS brand principles shown in their running shoes, and so would itself resemble a high-tech, beautifully designed piece that combines nature with technology in its aesthetics. This proactive product has a streamlined carbon-fibre frame combined with gels and durable padding.

Jaymes Schular
Industrial Design & Technology BA

Also on p.207

Hot Chocolate Carafe & Serving Set

Future design concepts for Cadbury

Since its introduction in Europe in the 1600s, hot chocolate has gone from being a drink of the nobility to a beverage that everyone can enjoy. This sweet and wholesome drink has long been seen as a comfort food and a treat, especially on cold winter evenings. Cadbury has long been a world leader in chocolate confectionery with their quality range of products to suit all tastes. It is not just the quality, but the fun that is associated with Cadbury products that has helped to make it a household name. With hot chocolate evolving from a winter warmer to an everyday drink that can be enjoyed at any time, what better inspiration for a new product that embodies the values of Cadbury.

This future concept for Cadbury is based on bringing people together and allowing them to share the fun. Hot chocolate can be prepared in different ways, and this concept allows you that flexibility. But the emphasis here is on the ritual of preparation, the joy of presentation and the reward of knowing you've made the perfect cup up of cocoa.

Andrew Bailey
Industrial Design BSc

Modern lifestyle is a busy one for most, too many people struggle to find the time for a bit of peace and quiet. In those precious minutes, what can be better than sitting in a comfy chair with an open book in your lap and a drink in your hand? E-books are cost effective to publish and environmentally friendly. However existing e-readers suffer from over complicated interfaces and a limited battery life when compared to a conventional book. Unlike conventional e-readers, the Cadbury Interlude does not force its users to stare at a dim and flickering screen, or go through a process equivalent to cracking a safe just to try and turn a page. Instead, it utilises smart paper technology, and literally prints any book onto photochromic pages. Once loaded from a PC, these pages do not require any power and the interlude will look and feel like conventionally printed publication.

Cadbury Interlude combines the versatility and technology of an e-reader with the unique quality of a printed book to deliver a full sensory experience that is wholly Cadbury.

Terence J Lee
Industrial Design BSc

Also on p.78

Cadbury Petal
Future design concepts for Cadbury

Based 15 years into the future, this design is for the Cadbury brand, now fully integrated within Kraft. Cadbury will be designing products in the context of high cocoa prices and low levels of profit gained. With the brand based on the aspect of a bit of fun everyday, and still trying to retain its values and identity to keep its old loyalty base, with the redirection of "finding your Cadbury place" to keep the essence of fun or joy in everyday life.

Aimed towards 8 to 12 years old girls, the Cadbury Petal is a portable projector shaped as a flower petal that opens up. With the imagery changing depending on nearby by petals belonging to friends, their own personal or social place, home or memories can be taken everywhere. While there is the ability to make a flower out of 8 petals and a central pod, you can create lots of shapes and fun. Cadbury petal enables girls to take a changing piece of their world with them everywhere.

Annabelle Spender
Industrial Design & Technology BA

Also on p.210

In the future life will become even more rushed and hectic for people working as nurses, carers, and in other caring professions. With an expected increase in the number of people over 50, making them a much higher proportion of modern society, there may well be a need for a large expansion in the caring industry.

The Cadbury Snooze is designed to enable people to drift off and 'find their Cadbury place' using the latest Eleksen technology and meditation music. This enables busy, hardworking users to enhance their well-being, becoming refreshed and able to carry on after a relaxing nap.

Also on p.204

John New
Industrial Design BSc

Future Concepts For PIMM'S

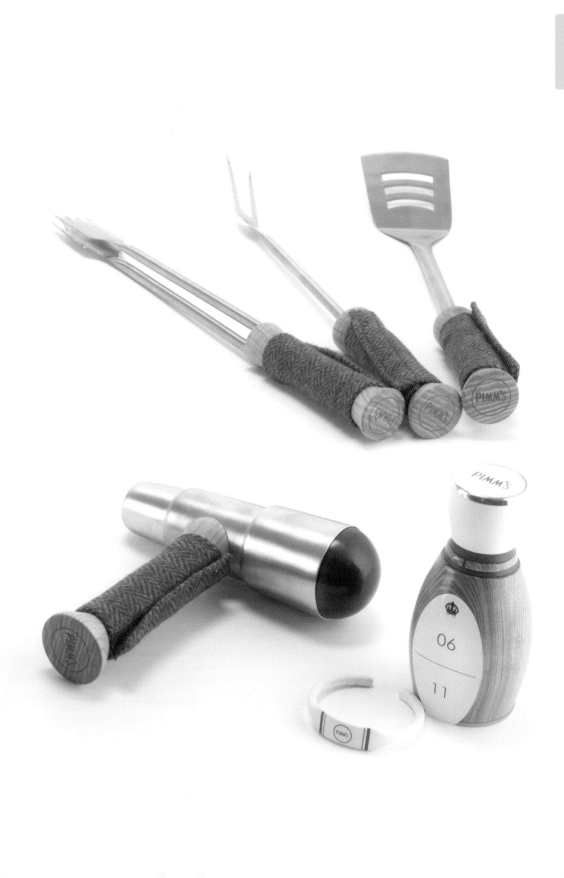

PIMM'S Clock
Future design concepts for PIMM'S

Working environments such as the office can be mundane and dull. It is also the case that work related pressures lead to high stress levels, and are linked to health issues, which heavily affect a person's level of well-being. The new PIMM'S Clock concept encapsulates the brand's ethos of creating a heightened sense of community, social empowerment, and well-being. This product detects the mood of each individual present and outputs a colour to express the combined spirit of the team, encouraging a united group effort to achieve and maintain a positive state of mind. PIMM'S Clock posesses the charismatic quality and style associated with the PIMM'S brand. The Clock demonstrates deep understanding of the user requirements, and introduces the PIMM'S effect into the office. It works to bring a heightened sense of community and increased social empowerment, ultimately resulting in an improved level of well-being.

Jonathan Aihun
Industrial Design & Technology BA

Also on p.27

This project focuses on well being, and how it can be used to further enhance the PIMM's brand.

We are witnessing a large demographic shift across the world, with older people expected to increase more than double by the 2030. Older people are fitter, healthier and wish to remain happy and have the same high quality of life, despite of the mental and physical challenges associated with later years.

PIMM'S utensils encourage greater social interactions and promote well being. The PIMM'S effect is all about excitement togetherness and fun.

Food can be used to create social scenarios and share the PIMM'S Effect, transforming a typical mundane situation into interesting and memorable events.

Neepun Goyal
Industrial Design & Technology BA

PIMM'S Medical Wristband
Future design concepts for PIMM'S

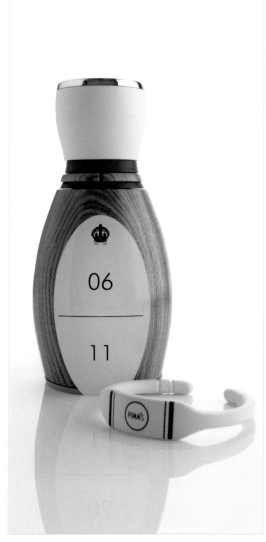

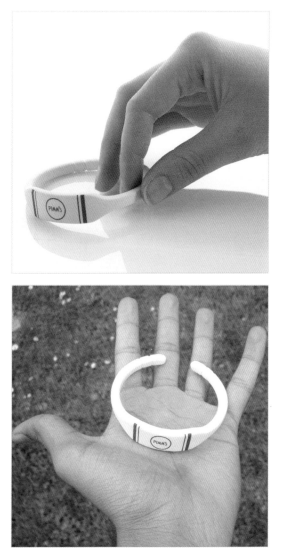

In the future we risk drifting further apart as society and as individuals. The PIMM'S Effect is about connecting and creating new relationships to make a positive impact on the future. Hospitals are one of those rare opportunities to meet and interact with new people. The wristband brings the distinctive PIMM'S brand of quirkiness and humour to provide social empowerment to patients.

The PIMM'S medical wristband changes what we expect a medical wristband to be. It actively warms our skin when worn, while monitoring the patient's health and location. This information is continuously relayed to healthcare staff. The bands also act as racquets for an augmented reality game, a good old game of badminton.

The Wristband is made of piezoelectric material which allows the band to change shape to wrap around the patients wrist and to be flat packed for storage. The PIMM's posts are used to setup the size and position of the court as well as keeping score of the game.

Sahil Nurmohamed
Industrial Design BSc

PIMM'S Wimbledon helps people to be more sociable on public transport. The idea is based around the new high-speed rail lines that will be cropping up all over the world during the next 20 years. This would see people having similar length journeys to planes but with more space and in more comfort.

This is an interactive gaming solution using the table as a projected screen and a number of controllers that people would hire to control the play. The game would be branded and contain such sports as tennis, croquet, golf, cricket, any sport with a British connection. The product would use Wiiesque controllers to avoid the negative connotations that have devleloped around consoles such as a XBox or Playstation and instead be a service to everyone. The product will aim to bring people taking long journeys on trains together though modern technology and an innovative approach to it. Anyone for PIMM'S Wimbledon?

Joe Snowdon

Industrial Design BSc

Also on p.39

Rub the Right Way...
Future design concepts for Playboy

Rub the Right Way... is a future concept for the Playboy brand that specifically targets elderly couples, encouraging individuals to reconnect with each other in order to reinvigorate relationships, resulting in increased emotional and physical wellbeing.

Incorporated haptic technology simulates the feeling of being stroked by your partner when it is physically impractical or alternatively when you are spending time apart, promoting emotional rekindling.

When used collectively, vigorous interaction provokes the gentle secretion of massage oils allowing the parts to be used in an intimate setting if desired. Combined the product aims to spark physical interaction, increased confidence and pleasure.

Sharan Kaur
Industrial Design & Technology BA

Also on p.75

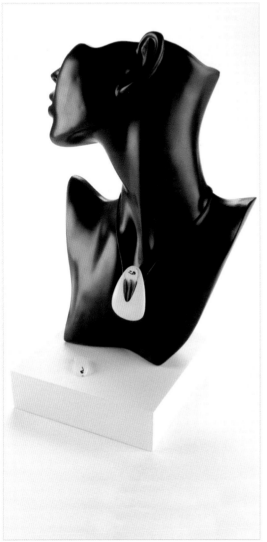

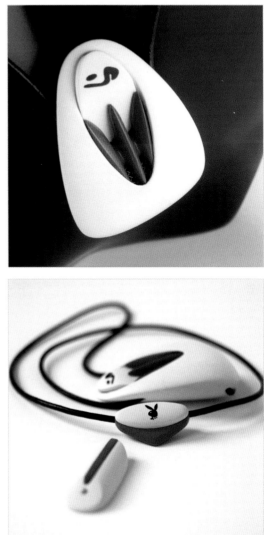

A wearable romantic catalyst designed for couples who have recently had a child. The Heat of the Moment is part of the product range for the 2020 vision of the Playboy franchise.

Time is precious with a third person now in the relationship, though the spark between the couple still exists. The Heat of the Moment drives intimacy and reinvigorates the relationship when there is special time to be together.

The couple wear a pendant each which when in close proximity release a male/female pheromone. The unisex design and interchangeable pheromone capsule allows people of both genders and sexual orientations to share the experience with their partner. This product plays to the strengths of technological advances by the year 2020 such as the rise in biotechnology and advanced manufacturing methods.

Peter McClelland
Industrial Design BSc

Also on p.196

Forbidden Fruits
Future design concepts for Playboy

Forbidden Fruits aims to reintroduce the spark between couples by providing a novel and cheeky way of enhancing the quality of the time spent together, especially in the bathroom. Through the use of ultrasonic technology, your partner can become aroused by a flick of a button, targeting the erotic zones with different intensities and through various textures. As one partner is in control of the other, secret inhibitions can be released, breaking down barriers and improving overall sexual well-being.

Forbidden Fruit enhances the couples' relationship when they are experiencing "empty nest syndrome". Now that they have space at home, the couple realise that they do not know as much about each other as they thought. Time and money have always been centred on their children, what do they do now? Often one of the partners may be at work, whilst the other is left unoccupied alone at home. Although both partners love each other, they are not used to communicating intimately. Forbidden Fruits breaks down inhibition barriers such that their relationship stays strong.

Christopher Harkin
Industrial Design & Technology BA

Also on p.190

In the world of 2020 technological advances will push people's time and relationships to the limit. As part of a proposed repositioning of the Playboy brand, this product will allow its owners to communicate in a flirty way, even while apart. The product helps couples get their spark back if they are perhaps spending too much time at work, and not enough with each other.

The pen is used to write messages to your partner, which are then sent directly to their screen. When it is received the wireless OLED screen 'zips up', ready for them to reveal the message when the time is right. They just run their finger down the screen to un-zip it down to its fabric like base, revealing the message that's provocatively hidden underneath. You can leave the message exposed, or choose to zip it up again to keep those more saucy messages between just the two of you…

Stephanie Fox
Industrial Design & Technology BA

Also on p.188

Design with Intent
Influencing people's behaviour through products and services

Design inevitably influences our behaviour, whether we notice it consciously or not. As you walk around Made in Brunel, you can be sure that your attention and interest as well as the route you take around the show will be shaped, on many levels, by the design and positioning of the stands, the colour and style of the display boards, the appearance of the projects (and the people!).

As designers we do not always consciously consider the power this gives us to help people (or, indeed, to manipulate them), but there is growing recognition that "designers are in the behaviour business", championed by people such as Frog Design's Robert Fabricant and Stanford's BJ Fogg with the concept of persuasive technology. I have used the term 'Design with Intent' to mean design that is intended to influence, or result in, certain user behaviour. It is an attempt to describe systems across lots of disciplines—services, products, interfaces, even built environments—that have been designed with the intent to influence how people use them.

However, there is not much guidance available for designers briefed with influencing users' behaviour, particularly in socially beneficial humanistic contexts, such as reducing the environmental impact of our everyday lives (the focus of my research here at Brunel). As consumer products become increasingly efficient technologically, human behaviour is often the weak link at a societal level, but also at the scale of interaction with individual products and services. We buy 'energy-saving' lights and then leave them on all night, boil a kettle-full of water even though we only need a mug-full and stick with the default setting on the washing machine, afraid of investigating the others. Individual behavioural decisions (or the lack of them) are responsible for a significant proportion of our energy use and waste generation, and in many ways encouraging more sustainable behaviour can be seen as a design problem, concerned with how and why people interact with the products and systems around them, and how that interaction might be influenced.

Some of the fantastic student projects you can see in this book are addressing exactly this area: helping people to use resources more effectively, from reducing household water consumption to using household heating more efficiently. Others are tackling other kinds of socially beneficial behaviour change through design, from helping people to drink more water, to encouraging people in public toilets to wash their hands and to motivating busy parents to spend more time with their children.

In fact, the concept of design explicitly intended to influence users towards particular behaviours recurs across a number of disciplines, from the growing field of design against crime, to urban planning encouraging community spirit, to mobile phone applications making it easier to track your exercise regime, to getting people to sign up correctly on websites, to the fact that cash machines make you take your card back before giving you cash. But not much work has been done to link ideas and techniques from these disparate fields—ergonomics, behavioural economics, human-computer interaction and cognitive, social, and ecological psychology—and present them in a form which can be applied by designers to develop new products and systems, or improve existing ones.

This is what I have been trying to do via my research, which has led to the development of the Design with Intent toolkit (http://www.designwithintent. co.uk): a pattern library of techniques for influencing behaviour though design, with diverse examples from many different domains presented in a form which is hopefully useful to designers as a way of generating relevant ideas and suggesting new ways to address problems where human behaviour is an important component. (It ought to be applicable to design for behaviour change in general, not just more sustainable behaviour, although that is the focus of my PhD as part of the Cleaner Electronics Research Group).

The patterns (over 100 so far) are grouped into 'lenses'—currently Architectural, Errorproofing, Interaction, Ludic, Perceptual, Cognitive, Machiavellian and Security—as a way of explaining them via different worldviews, both representing and challenging preconceived ideas clients might have about how to influence users. The examples show how analogous or similar problems have been tackled by designers elsewhere—and how effective the solutions have been.

Over the last couple of years, Design with Intent has been tested and developed through workshops with designers, design students and other stakeholders.

There have also been some great opportunities to demonstrate it to organisations such as the RSA, IDEO London, QinetiQ, Learndirect, EMC Consulting and Engine Service Design as well as running sessions here at Brunel for Sustainable Design and Environmentally Sensitive Design modules on our MSc Integrated Product Design and BA/BSc Design courses. It has been applied to briefs ranging from getting people to shower for less time, to closing curtains at night to conserve heat, to influencing people not to leave the tap running while brushing their teeth, with hundreds of new concepts generated and evaluated. At the time of writing I am preparing to run a workshop at the UX London conference, applying Design with Intent to the design of online user experience—helping guide and support users' decision-making via websites and improving usability whilst influencing behaviour.

Along with my Brunel Design colleagues Fergus Bisset—who is investigating intrinsic motivation through design—and Nicola Combe, who is working with Buro Happold on bringing together inclusive and sustainable design through better home heating controls, and other colleagues in the Human Centred Design Institute here at Brunel, we are trying to push forward the frontiers of what is an exciting, fast-developing new kind of design thinking and practice. Politicians are starting to talk a lot about behaviour change for social benefit: if they are serious, designers of the future are going to be crucial to this effort.

Herbert Simon—one of the most brilliant interdisciplinary minds of the 20th century—once said that "everyone designs who devises courses of action aimed at changing existing situations into preferred ones", and this applies to designing behaviour just as much as it does to physical features. Whether we mean to do it or not, it is going to happen, so we might as well get good at it.

By Dan Lockton

Dan Lockton is a PhD researcher in the Cleaner Electronics Research Group, Brunel Design. He studied BSc Industrial Design Engineering at Brunel, and then a Cambridge-MIT Institute Master's in Technology Policy at the University of Cambridge. Before returning to Brunel in 2007, Dan worked for clients including Sinclair Research and Tangerine on consumer technology and lightweight transport research and development.

The Design with Intent toolkit is available from http://www.designwithintent.co.uk

Beauty Through the Eyes of a Product Designer

Visual Beauty

Each and every one of us has a slightly different perception of beauty; what one person may find beautiful another may have no interest in at all. This simple fact makes understanding the definition of beauty a very complex and difficult process. There are a huge range of variables which affect the way people view objects and the experience which each individual has whilst studying or using a specific product. Although it is very difficult to pin point exactly what makes people find certain things beautiful, it is possible to gain an understanding of where attraction, as an instinct, and the society around us has affected the way we look at the world and judge the beauty of almost everything in it.

This article is an exploration into people's aesthetic judgements, what we find beautiful and why. Looking at a range of sources from evolution, instincts and the world around us, to our current environments, lifestyles and trends, will provide better understanding of which product styles are more likely to attract specific groups or individuals.

Many people believe that the initial stages of sexual attraction play a large part in determining what we enjoy looking at and therefore which products we are attracted to. The reason that attraction to the opposite sex is so relevant when comparing the raw feeling of attraction to the aesthetics of designed products is that the early stages of sexual attraction are often purely the result of a visual stimulus. We are initially attracted to someone because of their looks and possibly what they are wearing. The instantaneous notion of whether a person is attractive or not closely relates to the feeling we get when we first look at a product. Our judgement based on what a person is wearing is more subjective, this is based on whether we think a person dresses well and whether they're fashionable. By studying a person's dress sense it's possible to make a series of assumptions about that person. Their style and choice of clothing often indicates what their personal interests may be. Similarly if the style of a product relates well to your style you're more likely to be attracted to it.

Throughout our lives our opinions on what we visually like and dislike will develop gradually, the nature of this progression is all dependent on the experiences we have in our lives; moving to a new place, meeting new people and the development of fashion through time, I feel are three of the most influential drivers for change in aesthetic opinion.

Aesthetic Design

Creating an aesthetically positive design is often key to a design's success. Not only are people attracted to things which look nice but people perceive more aesthetic designs to be easier to use and we're also more likely to use them. This phenomenon is known as the aesthetic usability effect, not only does it state that people are more trusting of products with positive aesthetics but that we're generally more empathetic with product failings.

The relationship that a user has with a design directly affects the way in which they interact with it, having a positive relationship with a product generally catalyses creativity and problem solving, whereas a negative relationship narrows thinking and stunts creativity.
(Universal Principles of Design, 2003).

To design an excellent product an amalgamation of aspects must work together seamlessly and efficiently. These aspects are specific to each product. Alignment is one of the most basic principles of aesthetic success, making the visual composition of a product flow is a very subtle but important consideration for designers. Placing product elements in a balanced relationship with each other and using tone and colour to create a good composition make a product, or a painting or photograph pleasurable to look at. Although balance and composition must always be a consideration for designers, it can often be more important to have a perfectly functioning product than a beautiful one. There needs to be a perfect balance between visual beauty and functional performance which makes superb products.

Beauty is huge in society today, with the emergence of television, the Internet and the general growth of global tools of communication, we've enabled the media to affect the world far more than it ever used to. The pressure on people to look good appears to be a permanent addition to society. Although it is healthy for people to care about their appearance and general wellbeing the amount of emphasis the media puts on being skinny and beautiful is not such a good thing. The media is full of good looking and successful people, through constant exposure to this we, the public, are made to feel inferior.

The media's rose tinted screen alters the perception of everyone exposed to it, because we are all so used to seeing beautiful people on a daily basis people's appreciation of beauty has diminished.

Although the media is a very valuable rescource for todays designer it is not something we can control, it allows us to predict trends and understand specific details about peoples aesthetic judgment. We as designers must be careful not to fall into the trap of interpreting the media's portrayal of aesthetic brilliance as the public's views.

In terms of promoting or making a product more attractive, advertising and the media is an excellent tool. Designers and marketing personnel are able to engineer the way in which a product is portrayed by society, this is where a deep understanding of what people find attractive and why it is so important. If a product is beautifully designed and well promoted it's likely to be successful, providing that the product concept is something which people could want; unfortunately, from a sustainability point of view, products are not always things people need.

Beauty in Relation to Design

Do designers view beauty differently to everyone else? Perhaps because beauty is so integral to the success of stylists' professions they treat it with more respect and consideration. Anyone who uses visual communication in relation to aesthetics in their everyday lives will see beauty in a more complex and different light to someone who views objects without consideration for product aesthetics. For any designer who is involved in the creative visual process it's important to have a grasp of what makes things beautiful, and also to have defined opinions on how to use the right kind of beauty in their products.

Throughout history designers and artists have taken inspiration from the natural world. Understanding the ways in which the media, our physical environment and society affect our visual judgements, along with studying relevant and beautiful elements in nature; is a valuable process which will push product aesthetics gradually closer to the beauty which people desire. As designers learn more about the psychological progression of people, products will become better suited to their target markets and should be more pleasurable in every aspect.

Scraping the surface of several aspects of visual beauty in today's society has emphasized the fact that it is impossible to please everyone with a single product. Opinions will always vary, which creates much needed diversity in the product world.

Being empathetic towards our environment and appreciating the world around us will always help facilitate good design; by studying the earth's beauty, designers have been able to invent beautiful and timeless products; understanding the effects of social values and our society opinions will enable us to gain a deeper understanding of the differences in opinions on aesthetic beauty. The impossible task of dissecting the workings of evolution is possibly the key to fully understanding what we truly find beautiful and why.

By Francis Lofthouse

The Metrosexual Man
A by-product of second-wave feminism?

Since the rise of second-wave feminism, demands on men by women have arguably developed into unrealistic expectations. Women appear to want the impossible. Men still identifiably male, confident, successful, independent, yet at the same time well groomed, sexy, domesticated and in touch with their emotions.

Modern man has become increasingly influenced by the rising consumer culture. This hyperconformance has had a dramatic effect on the mental health of the male population as shown in the quadrupling of suicide rates, causing many to become uncertain about their masculinity or role within society. Men have changed over the past thirty years into a new species, half-man, half-woman, otherwise known as the metrosexual. This terminology was created in 1984 by journalist Mark Simpson:

"Metrosexual Man: A single young man with a high disposable income that lives or works in the city because that's where all the best shops are."

Initially, gay men provided guidelines for many heterosexual men to follow. They were single, socially independent, men that knew how to accessorise and look good at the same time. Men sought to adopt the style of these openly gay men as a way of advancing themselves in an increasingly visual, aesthetic and arguably shallow world.

One can argue that consumer capitalism created metrosexuality, turning modest straight males into a new kind of man, less certain of his identity and correspondingly much more interested in his own image. According to Freudian theory most of these new found shopping habits are due to the new homosocial culture that has required adult masculinity to evolve. Men are now fashioning their masculinity using celebrity guidance and lifestyle magazines to impress the opposite sex.

Mark Simpson describes metrosexual man as a commodity fetishist that purely desires the male

fantasies marketed to him through the media and advertising; "There is a peacock factor; men want to preen their feathers so they appeal to the opposite sex. Footballers and actors will always use a skincare and make-up line and men follow those role models. They mimic the success by buying the clothes their role models wear and emulating their grooming. They want to be David Beckham or whoever it is."

According to Jeanne Marecek and Victor Seidler, the male world was tragically compromised by the second-wave feminist movement. Apparently, new found self-confidence within women enabled them to gain an upper hand in family life, resulting in men losing their vitality, direction and individuality. Many men were often made to feel guilty, confused and uneasy about their actions. Jeanne and Victor both perceive that this in return was an enslavement of men.

Traditionally, masculinity was based upon several factors including: physical strength, resourcefulness, stoicism, and pragmatism. Employment was used as a strong prop for masculinity, a 'successful man' was expected to provide for the family. However, the masculine breadwinner role was broken down by women when they began to work. At the same time, men were expected to retain their finicial independence thus leaving them free to decide for themselves and to make executive decision for the family to try and fill a more domesticated role, helping with the housework and childcare. The problem was that men were reluctant to assume their domestic responsibilities at the same rate as women entering the workforce. This was further exacerbated by the economic downturn of the 1970's, calling the models of masculinity and femininity to be readdressed.

Men are now lagging behind women in every major category from lifestyle to health, education to employment. Since the 1970's, the rise in divorce rates and widespread use of contraceptives have led to an absence of fathers, causing a major shift in the productive sphere towards the apparent advantage of females. With IVF, men have been rendered almost completely dispensable, meaning that survival of the fittest has resulted in the evolution of the metrosexual man.

Is this what women want? Women seem confused about what they want men to be, which has not been helped by the media. Men originally were portrayed throughout the media as being powerful, dominant, heroic and successful, helping to maintain a consistent identity for influential men and women to follow. However, social evolution has caused these attributes to now be portrayed negatively within the media. Some will argue that this has gone too far.

Paul Nathanson and Katherine Young state that worldwide views on our society seem to have become "increasingly both gynocentric (focused on the needs and problems of women) and misandric (focused on the evils and inadequacies of men)."

Many western men feel vulnerable and confused about their purpose, worried that they cannot speak their minds or act without being chauvinistic. In 2008 a UK Daily Telegraph survey demonstrated 52% of the men surveyed said that they had "to live according to women's rules" and only 33% felt that they could "speak freely about what they thought." More than half of the men surveyed thought society had turned them into waxed and coifed metrosexuals.

The objectification of men in women's magazines and mass media that has arisen over recent years is clearly exampled in programs such as Sex and the City, where modern men are often portrayed as purely sex objects - used for aesthetic appeal, amusement and pleasure. Although this can be taken in jest, some have taken it much further, including author Susan Faludis in her bestselling book 'Stiffed: The Betrayal of Modern Man'. She states that society has changed from producing a culture, to a culture rooted in no society at all. Global corporatism was to blame because it helped to sweep away many of the institutions, unions, veteran associations, political and civic groups, that gave western men a sense of belonging. Instead, a dysfunctional pseudo evolved, encouraging men to purchase consumer goods to fill this void, making them concentrate more on their looks rather than on their jobs. She does not agree that men have become soft, but argues instead that they have been strategically manipulated into a lifestyle sold to them through advertisement and celebrity endorsements. Men are not so foolish as to believe that the products which have emerged from this will turn them into the next Jude Law! Instead, culture has reshaped their sense of manhood by stating that masculinity is something that can be worn, not drawn from within.

Positive portrayal of modern man can be seen through lifestyle magazines like Esquire and Men's Health which help to provide guidance for men on a range of issues concerning sex, health and fashion. The fact that men are buying these magazines demonstrates that many men have changed into metrosexuals because they have actually wanted to!

The 1973 Berkeley Men's Center Manifesto finally enabled men to take back their full humanity and express exactly how they feel. In the same way that feminism enabled women to break away from society's constraints, the new metrosexual movement enabled men to no longer feel that they need to comply with the stereotypical masculine image of being strong, silent, unemotional and successful.

Feminism has indeed inspired, but not caused, masculinity to evolve. Many men wanted this to occur. They realised that society would benefit from the improvements gained by liberating women's rights and therefore became easily persuaded to embrace this social revolution, letting go of the traditional restrictions placed upon them.

Masculinity has not been lost, but has evolved into androgyny, allowing men to adopt feminine traits within a new found social role. It seems that as long as femininity exists, masculinity in some form will always be there to hold its hand. Younger men in particular seem to be leading this revolution, portraying a clear generational shift that has redefined the terminology for masculinity and also perceived sexuality.

Evidence suggests that the metrosexual man has indeed been crafted out of the second-wave feminist movement, which could be purely down to the fact that men just want to look as good as women in today's world. Fundamentally, the root of any form of heterosexual masculinity is the sexual relationship between a man and women. It does not matter what reposition it may be: Metrosexuality, Retrosexuality, Neosexuality, or the recently announced Ubersexuality, society will never agree on its exact role. It will be constantly influenced by social structures like education, friendship groups, mass media and employment, to evolve and continue to survive within an ever changing world.

By Christopher Harkin

humanistic innovation

Masters Research in
Design Strategy,
Innovation & Branding

The last ten years has witnessed a transformation in Design Strategy. It has moved from simply considering artefact, space or communication, to becoming essential in the building of intangible values into brands, IPR, and culture. It has also extended its influence beyond the profit driven world into public services and social change. The following research topics reflect and push our understanding of these changes and also the continuing drive for design, to build people into solutions. The projects aim to explore emerging techniques such as participatory design and the search for ways of embedding humanistic values like trust, integrity and intimacy into our created worlds.

Deepening knowledge and understanding of Design Strategy implies engaging with thought leaders and experts from the world of design and branding. We are grateful to those who have offered contact and support in this area. Here SungHan Kim, Head of Samsung Design Europe, offers a perspective on design and brand strategy

Brand value and design value

Business Week and Interbrand, the London-based brand strategy consultancy, have released the annual ranking of the 100 best global brands. The 2009 release ranks Samsung's $17bn brand value 19th out of 100. Brand valuation is based on a brand's estimated future financial value, driven by the elements which persuade customers to purchase a particular brand. 'Design' and 'Brand' are clearly recognised key drivers, amongst others in this systemic approach. An interesting finding is that interrelated key drivers collaboratively influence customer choice decisions. Predictably, design recognisably contributes to Brand in conjunction with other drivers, including price and usability. Samsung's brand value of $17bn can therefore be partially attributed to design factors.

Apart from financial measurement of the cross-over between design and brand, the strategic design propositions in brand management and communication are already well known in the design profession; from the packaged brand identity design to product portfolio design. I believe that the interface between design and brand is increasingly important in the current business context, because the topic of "Innovation through holistic user experience and storytelling", cited daily in design meetings, is concerned with 'design evolution'. From technology biased design innovation to customer communication, we need to focus on the immediate needs of design development strategy and process, integrated with brand strategy, or vice versa.

According to a recent Financial Times article, companies with stronger brand power (within BrandZ in the top 100) have been more successful than the S&P 500 average in 2010 total returns. (BrandZ companies score 18.5%, S&P 500 -11.5%) and those with more identifiable brand strengths have been proven to enable business survival during the recent severe economic recession, leading to successful resurgence. Branding thus appears to play an increasingly important role in the popular mindset and customer decision-making in the post-recession period. This clearly indicates greater challenges and opportunities for the implementation of design and brand-integrated strategies. Although design and brand are still disparate concepts in business operations, this presents an exciting opportunity for designers and design theorists to roll out further innovative and creative initiatives.

By SungHan Kim
Head of Samsung Design Europe

SungHan Kim graduated with top honours in Industrial Design from Kook-Min University, Seoul and received the Master degree in Design Methods from Illinois Institute of Technology, Chicago. After graduate study, he moved to London for the role of the head of Samsung Design Europe (SDE). His core interest is well aligned with SDE's challenge and strategic role. Its well established leadership in multidisciplinary design process and user centred design has successfully contributed to not only building next-generation innovative design but also envisioning the continuous growth of Samsung Design.

Honesty & Integrity in the world of Branding

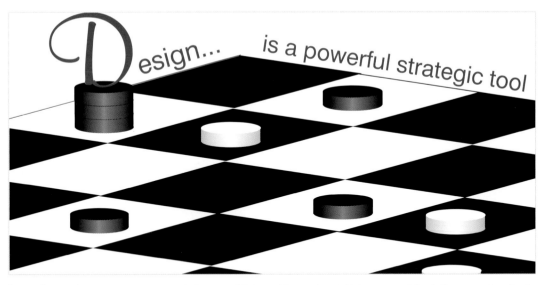

In a time when many commentators, within business and society at large, suggest that honesty and integrity are rare and undervalued concepts, this research project will identify the responsibility of design in creating honesty and integrity for brands. It will underline the importance of design in the world of branding and contribute to the understanding of how powerful design can be when used in the correct way. Secondary research is used extensively in identifying current thinking on ethics and honesty in branding from books, such as The Hidden Persuaders by Vance Packard, Beyond Branding by Nicholas Ind, The Manipulators by Jeffrey Robinson, articles and documentaries. Case studies, for example of Body Shop and BMW, will be examined with specific attention to the role of design in each. Interviews will be conducted to support further the case studies. Surveys in the form of questionnaires will be formulated to seek insights on customer's perception on the subject. Early findings from my research suggest that brands such as Waitrose, and BMW have gained a high degree of customers trust. It is also surprising what brands customers do not trust. A phrase that I have come across while researching and I believe is highly relevant, by Lucienne Roberts (2006, Good: An Introduction to ethics in graphic design) argues that "Design is to provide information not sugar-coated enticements". Professor Anthony Grayling (2006, Good: An Introduction to ethics in graphic design) also states that "design is neutral until the moment it is put into context".

Throughout this course I had the opportunity to work in teams with people from all over the world. For our Branding assignment we were divided into groups by our tutor so I had to work with people who until then were not my friends. But by working with different people for each group assignment I had the opportunity to understand and develop strong working relationships with many more of my classmates. The assignment was about an interview we had to conduct with a person actively engaged with the branding industry in order to identify the barriers, changes and future opportunities for branding. My group interviewed Justine Hofman, the marketing manager of Makedo, a company which produces constructive toys. I was impressed by how enriching, easy, but at the same time challenging it is to work with other people. We had our disagreements but I got to listen to other people's views who are involved in the same subject as me.

As part of our Design Futures module we had to attend a seminar where 8 people, authorities in the field of design, presented to us their thoughts about the future of design. There was one person who for me stood out and impressed me the most, Lady Kitty Chisholm. She talked about how we as new designers should "design ourselves to create the emotions towards us". What our goals should be and where we have to focus in order to evolve as designers and as human beings.

Alexia Kedra
MA Design & Branding Strategy

Branding like Video Gaming
A brand Model inspired by the success of the gaming industry

Video gaming is a huge industry around the world nowadays. It is growing, and every day more and more people join this massive market as consumers. Most of the people are emotionally involved with games, and gaming has moved beyond being just fun to being a holistic experience. For a long time video games were influenced by everything in the world like books, movies and human behaviours. However this paradigm is shifting everyday, as the world is starting to become more aware of this market and today reality is beginning to get influenced by video games. There are lots of reasons why people are getting attached to video games. To create a successful video game, certain criteria need to be fulfilled. For example, it should have a strong narrative, it must give immediate feedback to the player about achievements and failures, and the complexity should increase step by step. The answer that I am chasing with my research project is - can we create branding strategies and business models based on successful criteria used in the design of video games? The potential outcome would increase the emotional depth of today's understanding of branding and the created brand framework can benefit companies trying to build a new brand. If we can apply video games' human centric nature and strong emotional stimuli into branding, we can create successful branding strategies through this framework. To create such a framework, I am bringing together the views of industry experts and extreme users through interviews with video game developers, gaming design experts, pro and casual gamers and brand strategists. Although society

does not fully understand the potential of video games as yet, as the famous futurist, inventor and author Ray Kurzweil says "If you want to see the future, keep your eye on the development of video games." This project is seeking an answer to the question - Can we also find the future of branding in video game design?

In my futures group assignment, we were trying to develop a future forecast for video gaming experiences. In this project, we conducted interviews with industry experts and gained invaluable insights. But the most educative part of the project for me was the group discussions we had. Some of my colleagues showed me that even though they had limited knowledge about the subject, through creative thinking and design vision they could contribute brilliantly. This experience proved to me once again that creative thinkers and design strategists can contribute in every industry even the ones they are not very well aware of. Through my master activities, one of the most influential activities was our Design Futures seminar. From all inspiring speakers, the Neal Stone's seminar was the most interesting for me. His ideas about how design is regularly misunderstood and how the definition of design needs to change explain the major problems of most designers today.

Arda Sesli
MA Design & Branding Strategy

Brand Trust & Integrity
Global Lifestyle Changes

This research will aim to create a brand strategy, using design and thinking techniques, to develop and maintain trust within the brand consumers relationship. My aim is to deeply understand the psychological and social reasons why people trust brands and products and what are the key cultural differences that influence these feelings.

As brand expert, Wally Olins and others have frequently said "Trust is the key for any successful relation in this fast changing multicultural world". Brands need to evolve and have a global understanding of consumer lifestyles to succeed in this unstable environment.

In order to explore an evolving society an exploratory study following the inductive approach, starting from the user experience, has been used. For the purpose of the research a combination of qualitative and quantitative research has been adopted, ethnographic research and participatory workshops where users had key role.

This methodology, known as mixed research is considered by experts (Creswell 2007) to be extremely valid because the data collection and selection is particularly accurate and user centered. The initial research suggests that there is a strict connection between the product experience and brand trust, moreover primary research shows that brand trust is handed down from generation to generation. In depth research also underlines the fact that historically banks were the most trusted institutions but turns of events change this perception, so it is possible to state that there is a shift in how trust is perceived and reflected by consumers based on current events and media influences.

If brands want to be 'on top of the game' they need to be trusted and evolve with time, as Niall Fitzgerald, chairman of Unilever, states "A brand is a storehouse of trust that matters more and more as choices multiply ".

Within the MA program I took part into the Multidisciplinary Workshop organized by L'Ecole Nationale Superieure des Mines de Saint-Etienne and Brunel. This workshop was an unique opportunity that gave me the possibility to experience a multicultural and multidisciplinary environment while working on a process of co-creation and innovation. Brunel students working with ENSM engineers, on how to create "Materialized Digital Identities", gave me the

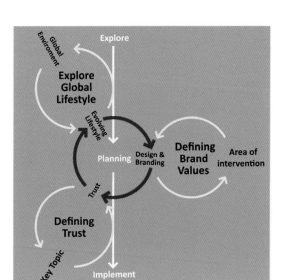

chance to quickly develop ideas into real concepts and understand the extremely notable value of the projects generated by this collaboration.

Contact with industry experts is a key component of the course. During my MA I interviewed Michael Wolff (Design and Brand Strategist , Owner of Michael Wolff & Company & Co-founder of the brand consultancy Wolff Olins). Michael is in an inspiring visionary that created iconic and unforgettable brand identities of our century.

During our interview we spoke about the relationship between creativity and design and how branding is related to social responsibility. This is one of the key insight of the interview, "Creativity to me means it wasn't there before. The think about creativity is that it is a choice and your imagination gives you the possibilities to make this choice and create what wasn't there before. Creativity is really about imagination and about new way to think about a company. It is a new way to look at what is around us. Design is the process of bringing creativity to reality."

Viviana Stecconi
MA Design & Branding Strategy

'In the old days, brands wanted everyone to pay attention to them. Now brands need to pay attention to everybody else.' (Frog Design, 2007)

There is a distinctive paradigm shift from brands having what we call target audiences, to brands now having a 'conversation'. Indeed now it is a partnership with their consumers.

The research looks at social media's influence in this digital age and how design is an underlying feature for authenticity and success in having a 'conversation' between brand and consumer. Consumers are buying into lifestyles of brands, so how can a brand digitally portray to a consumer its personality?

Philips Design (2001) gives a very interesting equation: BRANDING = DISTINCTIVENESS + AUTHENTICITY

It is this equation that provides a very interesting standpoint for design's influence on social media and its connection with the consumer.

Design is a valuable aspect because having a successful presence online is now the way forward. To be able to become effective, and maintain brand values and visions, it is important that design is integrated in the overall approach to provide 'distinctive authenticity' between brands for the consumer. Design is the key tool, to provide a distinctive, and consistent online presence. So in order to get this right, successful strategies need to be put in place. A new design-led branding strategy will be offered through modelling and integration of findings from interviews, questionnaires and secondary research.

The MA Design & Branding Strategy course provided a classic team working experience during the Design Futures module. Working within that team, has broadened my knowledge on the difference in cultures, and how design can be used to become more inclusive to all cultures whilst problem solving can develop very interesting concepts. The team generated novel ideas for a very interesting topic, which we entitled 'Intelligent Urbanism'. It involved the concept of having one"s belongings at a certain time and place, as and when you need them. Having a home wherever you are at the touch of button. Concepts were developed from trend spotting the rise of Globalisation, Consumerism, and Urbanisation in today's society…and looking at how a house can become a home, no matter where we are in the future.

Design Futures speaker Neal Stone influenced my thinking with his statement "as managers of design what we do must be measurable and effective, it is the key connector between creativity and business consulting."

Christina Daniels
MA Design & Branding Strategy

Brand Personality
How can contemporary design-led branding tools create personality?

The value of this research project lies in the formation of a design-led strategy for building a stronger brand personality. Classic brand texts such as 'Building Stronger Brands' (David Aaker, 1996) and the more recent work by Jennifer Aaker (1997) on 'Dimensions of Brand Personality' confirm that the concept of personality is highly complex when applied to brands. The beneficiaries of my research are brand managers and academics since the exploration of contemporary branding tools in relation to brand personality is still in its infancy, especially, when integrated with elements of design application, such as service and experiential design.

Research methods used include detailed analysis of case studies, for example, 'Marmite's Love it or Hate it' branding campaign and 'Cadbury's Dairy Milk' adverts. This enabled me to understand strategies from a secondary perspective, and it also allowed me to test my own hypotheses. Another method was conducting cultural and historical research into the theory behind personality. This was particularly useful in the early stages of research, when exploring the evolution of personality perception transfer from psychology into the marketing context.

The book-'Personality Not Included' by Rohit Bhargava (2008) has inspired my thoughts throughout this research. The following, quoted in Bhargava (2008) fuelled my aim and research question: "the biggest challenge most organisations face is discovering how to go from a brand that people consume to one that they are passionate about."

Gaining insights into brand personality creation involves analysing trends in contemporary branding tools which have grown due to increased usage of the Internet. One trend is the emerging importance of the 'accidental spokesperson' (Bhargava, 2008), for example, the 'The Unofficial Apple Weblog (TUAW)' is a blog that has become the unauthorised spokesperson for the 'Apple' brand (TUAW website, 2003). This trend is interesting as it poses opportunities and treats for the brand as they are giving up control of their own personality.

One of my memorable experiences on this course is the highly integrated team working aspect which takes place during the whole academic year. The Futures Assignment topic- 'The Future of Homes' -stands out for me since it presented the most challenges. The main issue was that we are all very ambitious and wanted a concept like no other and therefore, we were very critical of each other's contributions. This experience illustrates how team conflict is not necessarily undesirable as it pushes you to achieve better results.

This MA course has opened up many interesting avenues for learning; for example, I have been fortunate enough to hear from numerous industry professionals whom have contributed significantly to my learning. Deborah Dawton, who is CEO of the Design Business Association, spoke at the Design Futures seminar. Her speech was inspiring even though she was simply talking about the benefits of design which we learn about everyday. Dawton (2010) stated: "design has a very loud voice, be sure it shouts the right message" – this simple but profound message enhanced my own personal vision of design strategy thinking.

Christy Chung
MA Design & Branding Strategy

This research explores the combination of brand analysis tools and the designer's workflow during the early stages of 3D design projects. Designers effectively capture brand attributes in their work today, but I believe the process can be improved and that the improvement will benefit both designers and consultancies. By researching tools, categorizing their strengths, and developing frameworks around them, new methodologies could be created for 3D projects. For example, a designer could use combinations of the tools to rapidly analyze 'who' the client company is, what they stand for, and their aspirations. Once these brand elements are found, it could help communicate this knowledge with the client, project managers, and design team. With new tools to add brand elements into 3D design, there is potential to improve efficiency and produce work that effectively solves business challenges.

During the international EMSE Workshop, I joined designers, engineers, and brand strategists to explore the use of the new brainstorming tool by Synectics. The group spent a week at the French University developing ideas around the concept of "identity" in the modern world, aimed loosely at the telecommunication industry. We began with exercises capturing our thoughts on different aspects of the vague subject, which quickly developed into surprisingly rich and creative concepts. Both the use of the tool and working as an international team added valuable insights into today's design community and design techniques.

Several professionals, met through Brunel, were meaningful to me, especially those who had identified previously unseen opportunities for exploration in design. One standout was Paula Zuccotti, head of user research at Seymourpowell. She told me that during her time at Brunel she focused on ethnography, an emerging type of design research at that time. In the 10 years since, ethnography has become widely used in design and she is a leader in the specialty.

Travis Baldwin
MA Design & Branding Strategy

Engaging Gen-Y: New Design-led Branding
A Growing Social Group

Guy Garcia, CEO of MentaMetrix, introduced the concept of Gen-Y, people who were born during 1980's and early 1990's, during his speech about the impact of demographics in business, at the 56th annual convention of Advertising Research Foundation, 2010. He mentioned that the Gen-Ys, which only represented 15% of the population in 1999, represent the 49% of the population in 2010.

Today Gen-Ys are the market for many brands, and as they move to further stages of their lives, they will be the market for all other brands. In addition to their market size and the purchasing power, which is $200 billion annually only for college-aged Gen-Ys (Gardyn, Rebecca; "Educated Consumers"; American Demographics; 2002), their power over parental purchase, their role as the trendsetters and the early- adopters, make them the most coveted market segment. Yet their other characteristics such as their diversity and individualism; their interests in technology; the unknown motivations behind their consumption behaviours; their influence over the way humans interact; and their constant evolution, set challenges for the brands. Since building strong Brand Equity is getting difficult (Aaker, David; "Building Strong Brands"; 2002)are the present brand strategies still applicable when interacting with the Gen-Ys? Can design's role as a brand communication tool assist brands in this challenge? The objective of this research is to find answers to these questions by utilizing the most effective research methods, such as interviews with the representatives of both sides of this equation,

the Gen-Ys and brand leaders from companies such as SaatchiI&Saatchi, Brand Amplitude. The project will establish a deeper understanding of the scenarios in order to create a design led strategy for engaging brands with the Gen-Ys. In addition the project will improve brands' relationship with designers and design consultants.

Throughout my MA studies, I have come to understand the importance of the interaction between different backgrounds, ideas and cultures during the group works, which I participated. One particular cross culture project was the Design for Futures, in which we led a design research to improve the standard of living in places hit by disasters. I, therefore, want to demonstrate that an effective communication between different subjects as brands and design can result with a proficient tool when referring the Gen-Ys.

Since the beginning of my project, I have talked to many leading brand experts, specifically about the role of design. Carol Phillips is one of them, and she is the founder of Brand Amplitude. She described design's role as a catalyst that activates and speeds up brands' reaction with the Gen-Ys. She, however, touched upon the importance of service design and advised brands to point out their services when they are serving the Gen-Ys. Her interest in the Gen-Ys and her works on them have been a great influence on my research topic, which I believe will produce a unique insights.

Desiree Asena Dundar
MA Design & Branding Strategy

Brand Strategy & Design Collaboration through Storytelling

A good story moves us emotionally, but a great one has timeless relevance and value. My project aims to use storytelling to inspire design to not only innovative, but to also stay true to what a brand promises to its customers and society. Stories convey the goals of a brand's strategy and of its stakeholders by means of clear messages, without having to resort to technical jargon or perplexing charts and figures. The audience is able to pick up the essence of the brand, and create designs that are inspired rather than stifled by what the brand stands for. Design and brand managers can use storytelling to create powerful as well as timeless statements that continue to inspire different parts of an organisation.

In our Design Futures project we wanted to investigate how to improve food knowledge among urban dwellers. My group members, who came from countries from China to Israel, shared stories of how their culture taught the people about food, and these traditions and customs helped inspire our vision for the metropolises of the future. This taught me that there is an endless supply of human wisdom scattered among the people and cultures of the world, and all one has to do is open one's mind to learn.

When I attended the Design Futures seminar I felt very much inspired by how Neal Stone described the need for design business consulting. He knew that design could help businesses and brands succeed, but he also realised that there was a lack of people who could advise businesses on how to utilise design. This showed that the future of design needs to be more responsible and practical as well.

Toshiyuki Murata
MA Design & Branding Strategy

Multi-disciplinary Team Communication

Miscommunication between design and other disciplines in organisations can result in design mismatches, delayed processes and products poorly situated to market demands. Each discipline has their own aims and backgrounds, sets of skills, languages and jargons that may not be familiar with other disciplines and different thinking styles, for example designers are creative, engineers are concerned with accuracy and marketers are sales driven. This research aims to identify the communication difficulties and provide a framework for more effective communications through emerging methods and channels to ensure a more efficient NPD process.

With advancement in technology, new communication tools such as computer-based social networking methods emerged. Internal 'Jamming' and social networks such as 'Twitter' and 'Wiki spaces' are increasingly used to widen networking opportunities and to bridge the misconception between different disciplines through sharing of knowledge and expertise.

One of the design research methods used is role play conducted with a multidisciplinary team to work on various new-product development activities; the participants will be current students on the course, due to the diversity in their experiences and background. The purpose is to identify the communication difficulties and to discover new opportunities for improvements through observations.

During the course we had many opportunities for team working experiences; one of the most challenging tasks was to develop visions of the future. Our team agreed on exploring the issues caused by natural disasters in developing countries and how design can help create better shelters in the next 10 to 70 years. I have led in team meetings to develop strategic directions of the project, made sure our set objectives are met weekly and to use forecasting methods such as trends analysis and gathering expert opinions (Delphi). The most exciting part was the creative brainstorming session we had on scenario developments where we proposed unique design solutions. We strongly believe that the role of design is significant in the future, designers will identify genuine needs of people affected by natural disasters and will utilise new materials and technologies for developing safer shelters.

Over the period we had various guest speakers from the design industry to give us their personal insights. In particular, the Design Future seminar was most inspiring. One of the speakers was Neal Stone, former Head of Design at GNER and British Airways, gave a speech on how design should be the bridge between creativity and business consulting. He emphasized how design is often misunderstood as tangible output but in the field of design management, design operates at strategic level. Finally in his view, the future of design is vastly expanding from products and services into systems design, with reference to the successful innovation of Apple iTunes.

Julia Hamid
MA Design Strategy & Innovation

The digital revolution brought a new reality to the once wealthy Music Industry. Instead of buying albums out of impulse, people are exploiting the file sharing systems, accessing a massive amount of songs, bands and artists. Apart of all of the copyright debates, the consequences for the industry have been a matter of concern, since nowadays 95% of downloads are illegal and CD sales keep on falling.

However, this scenario also brought an opportunity. Studies presented in the book "Consuming Music Together: Social and Collaborative Aspects of Music Consumption Technologies" evidenced that music consumption is not only about buying and listening, but also about emotional connections, network building and definition of self-identity. If the mp3 files amplified the musical offer to each single consumer, it also "killed" the tangibles of this consumption, affecting directly the way people display their music collection.

To address this issue, the idea is to reshape an independent label business through design, by planning and creating a new set of tangibles for the global music consumption, and also by branding empowering the communication of intrinsic values of its specific genre (Rock and Roll), based in the successful case of Motown Records and the 4-D Branding and Lovemarks concepts.

To develop the ideas, an appropriate research will be conducted, including regular market techniques and also design research methods, such as cultural probe, focus group and social network content analysis.

One of the most important factors that will define the success of failure of this idea is the appropriate interpretation and understanding of the nowadays trends and the results that it might present in the future. In this sense, the group experience in developing future forecasting based in the trend analysis and specialists interviews was and will be extremely important to this research. Based in the mix of multicultural backgrounds and different visions of the videogame industry, the quality of the debate, the conclusions reached and the definition of the trends relevant to this field pointed important directions to this project, such as the future of Cloud Computing, interactivity and social networks. Some of these trends combined and created a phenomenon that already connects music and videogames industries: Guitar Hero and Rock Band.

These games pushed the music experience to another level. People now are not only passively listening, but also actively playing as a game and socially enjoying the experience. That is what people expect from music: not only to listen to it but to engage in a global experience. Stephen Izatt, Managing Director at Thinkfarm branding consultancy with large experience in the music industry and clients such as The Rolling Stones, Led Zeppelin, Bon Jovi and Oasis, in his portfolio, argues that live concerts are the top level of the music experience because people are surrounded by lots of different stimulus directed to different senses. The big profits come from product sales that encapsulates this memorable experience.

How to create that global experience and engagement with a label? That's the challenge.

Leonardo Simões Pinho
MA Design & Branding Strategy

Internal Branding in the Care Sector
Improving employee attitude and performance through design

"A brand is a promise of the goods and service a customer will receive from an organisation. If the organisation is to succeed, everyone working for the company must live and breathe the brand values" (Harkness, J, 1999)

"To take care of the customer, the organisation must first take care of those who care for the customer" (Papasolomou and Vrontis, 2006)

My aim is to find a means of implementing design in an internal brand strategy to ensure high levels of employee attitude and performance, and therefore enhance customer satisfaction as well as brand equity and loyalty. Due to the empathetic and emotional nature of the care sector, it is believed that any such method deemed suitable for this sector will translate into others and sensitively cater to the requirements of their stakeholders.

The long-term benefits of internal and behavioral branding have been proven by research, however, many companies still fail to understand the importance of adopting such strategies. This project will use design to make this area of branding more accessible for all internal parties involved, as no design-led branding model exists to make the process easier.

The primary advantage, to design, will be to demonstrate both its value and its role in countering a great variety of problems. When design is employed

in this way others profit; in this case, those in the care sector will benefit from the advantageous knock-on effects of a design-led model.

During the first semester we were required to complete many group projects. As none of us were familiar with each other, the majority of the group work was frustrating to begin with. One of the most stressful projects was one in which we were asked to combine features of Orange and T-Mobile in order to create a new brand strategy. The sheer weight of the work made the task difficult, however, over that time, we learned to pull together our talents and strengths, and ended up with an A grade Brand Strategy. The project gave us a chance to learn from each other, and although the task was testing, we gained a lot of satisfaction knowing that we had worked as a team to create a great piece of work. We became great friends as a result.

One of the most interesting developments of my MA learning was comparing what we had learned in lectures with professional industry practice. During interviews with Piers Guilar, (Senior Brand Strategist at Siegal and Gale), and Richard Worsley (of The Tomorrow Project) it became clear that some academic theories did not translate into practice. What inspired me most was the emotional commitment these individuals had with their work, it spurred me on to reach a deeper level in my own. Their passion drove them to fully understand their field and, in turn, made them leaders.

Marianne Catherine Waite
MA Design & Branding Strategy

Canvas

From the invention of the first Panel System during the late sixties (1968) until now, the vast majority of office furniture has maintained the same design principles. It is imperative to renew the design strategy for this sector and contribute to the evolution of solutions aligned to new trends and concepts.

The design research analyzes in depth the history and evolution of this sector. Firstly, in order to understand why it is so difficult to provide and adopt new schemes of working and secondly, in order to establish the grounds for a new design and branding proposal for Office Furniture industry.

Based on literature review, observation and interviews with management, marketing specialists, sales force and design experts; the research findings suggest workspace design must be fostered from different perspectives and new solutions should be presented with innovative approaches to customers. A major conclusion reveals that companies do not like changes and prefer to select traditional options which simply fulfil their basic needs. In addition, design is still considered a luxury and not an essential part of corporate strategy.

On the other hand, the project presents how evolution of our society demands positive changes according to its' needs, in this sense user-experience, demographic changes, technology and sustainability will influence the workspace panorama. Taking these points into account the investigation concludes with the commitment to reinforce the efforts to update the whole design strategy for this industry and implement truly relevant concepts for the benefit of all.

"To us, a human office is an environment that equally supports and makes sense to the individual and the organisation".

"Like a home, a human workplace is one that offers a variety of possibilities. In essence, what I am saying is that there is not one way of working. Work environments should recognize and reflect that we work in different ways throughout the day."
- Sevil Peach. Director of design studio Sevil Peach Gence Associates (SPGA) UK. 2009.

As a Colombian designer, I had the valuable opportunity to share new ideas and apply design thinking concepts with talented people in a new country with different backgrounds and ideas. Equally shaped by studies such as The Impact of Technology

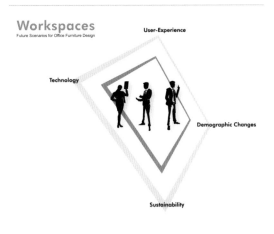

on Product Design (2030)

As a part of the module Design and Innovation Futures and along with five classmates we developed the relationship between technology and product design. It is without question a topic that affects our lives second by second. The results revealed a future vision where 3D immersive CAD, Co-Creation and The Maximization of Software will dominate this context. Nevertheless, we also concluded that human being must be the core of each new development and we cannot forget this premise.

"Design relies on humanising technology, not imposing technology on humans" - Bruce Nussbaum. Business Week, Innovation. USA. 2009.

At the Design Future Seminar 2010: "Sustainable Innovation - Developing Yourself"

Personally I found the idea to develop ourselves as sustainable innovators seriously interesting. As designers, we need to Identify, follow and protect our values. In the end that values will be key differentiators in our professional lives.

"Authenticity, Integrity and Congruence give us strength and focus." - Lady Kitty Chisholm. Development Strategy Advisor, HCDI, Brunel: Praxeis Coaching & Consulting. UK. 2010.

Mauricio Castaño Guiza
MA Design Strategy & Innovation

Terrain Vague
Design strategy to revitalize spaces

Post-industrial urbanization continues to create abandoned spaces that do not align with original functions, such as industrial facilities and infrastructures. With the coining of the French term "Terrain Vague," literature highlights the potential interest in public realms during the last fifteen years or so. Indeed, Tate Modern is regarded as the representative model of urban regeneration by transforming "Terrain Vague". These days, local governments are starting to consider benchmarking the Tate model focusing on economic regeneration, yet lacking a connection to socio-cultural sustainability. This research will assume that the involvement of communities in the whole design process is crucial for people-centred sustainability. For example, the case of "High line" in New York – the former 'abandoned railroad' - was preserved from demolition and rather transformed into one of the most innovative parks by the community itself. This research will investigate how people can take different views upon what exists in their community, and how creativity can be applyed to sustainable revitalization. In order to create a new design process, secondary research was conducted by literature reviews of books, journals and articles. Then as a primary research, case studies of community-led renewal projects, with interviews of academics, designers, and a governor, were carried out.

In the Design Futures research, my team proposed that design would help children by integrating social paths with technology in the future. We believe that Design should take part in identifying people who are excluded from society, such as isolated children, old people and disabled people, and involve them into the design process of inclusive products and services designed for the mainstream market.

Moreover, the focus of this research was supported in the discussion carried out by Jeremy Myerson, Director of Helen Hamlyn Centre, in the Design Futures seminar 2010. He underlined that the practice of Design should shift from designing 'for' people to designing 'with' and 'by' people in the future.

Ohram Kim
MA Design Strategy & Innovation

This research project strives to harness and channel design-led thinking and methodologies, in order to tackle one of the biggest challenges facing modern society; the delivery of healthcare.

In recent years, medical advances have led to an increased life expectancy. This shift towards an ageing demographic, coupled with changing lifestyles, means that the percentage of people suffering from chronic diseases such as diabetes and hypertension is on the rise. Today in England alone there are over 15 million people living with long-term health problems. In conjunction with mounting pressure for governments to cut expenditure, healthcare provisions must adapt to meet the changing needs of the patients and populations they serve.

In an attempt to modernise and improve efficacy, the healthcare sector is assuming a steadily increasing dependence on information technology; a factor that is rapidly transforming medical practice and the delivery of care. One of the key concepts emerging out of this synergy of technology and patient care is the notion of smart healthcare. The underlying concept seeks to utilise technology to enable the remote provision of healthcare services, irrespective of geographical constraints. This proposed interrelationship is receiving escalating levels of global attention from both the public and private sectors; a case heavily fuelled by numerous reports, which highlight the vast financial savings and improvements in the quality of care that could be achieved by transferring the treatment of many people from hospitals and residential care to private homes.

The concept of smart healthcare offers a radical, new model of health assessment that promises a non-obtrusive, patient-centred approach. It has the potential to provide accurate and reliable data to clinicians, while simultaneously empowering patients, influencing their attitudes and behaviours, and potentially improving their underlying medical condition and quality of life. But this is of little significance without wider dissemination to the general public.

Intelligent monitoring and control systems have, for a long time, been a major topic of medical research and a continuum of successful applications have been demonstrated over the past twenty years. Sustained developments and availability of electronics, information technology and communications

technology have made such projects increasingly feasible and cost effective. However, to date, countless attempts have failed to materialise beyond research and prototype status, and of those that have, very few have managed to become commercially successful.

There is a huge opportunity for smart healthcare to move into the mainstream, but this is entirely dependent on the way in which it is implemented. Acknowledgement of this forms the basis for an in-depth explorative study, which examines the complexities involved in transforming these concepts into highly relevant solutions that deliver true benefit to all concerned.

Following a strategic design-led approach, the project seeks to shed fresh light on the subject matter and leverage innovative thinking as the principle driving force. Creative tools will be used to uncover the multifaceted array of stakeholder requirements, and will culminate in the construction of an actionable strategic framework. By directly addressing some of the major barriers to acceptance, the project sets out to build an advisory platform that could revolutionise the way future generations of smart healthcare offerings are developed and deployed.

This study is being supported by the Technology Strategy Board and ESPRC funding bodies and is being conducted in conjunction with a live R&D project between a consortium of 9 leading organisations.

Oliver Wooderson
MA Design Strategy & Innovation

Branding Strategy Against Property Crime In Urban Areas

Building a strong community spirit, a long term solution against vandalism

Since 1981, property crime accounts for the majority of recorded crime in urban areas within the UK. During the recent decades, some cities have adopted design-led brand communication strategies to promote crime awareness. Nowadays, long term solutions will need a community design approach that gathers city planners and all stakeholders that impact on the daily lives of urban citizens. Consequently, the aim of this project is to conceptualize appropriate urban design metrics and evaluate their impact on the city brand image. The study encompasses a need to identify the role that all stakeholders and city-region decision makers have to play when designing strategies against vandalism. Furthermore, the research applies both secondary and primary research tools including for example contextual mapping of urban places in a London Borough that present a picture of the conflict and synergy between all stakeholders. Moreover, participatory studies were used to design with a hope of uncovering the latent needs of the residents. Finally, case studies are analysed to understand the issues that are influencing the efficiency of the decision-making process against urban vandalism in the cities of London, Singapore and Detroit. So far, the study reveals that efficient re-conceptualization of urban design including the design of the community spirit, are long term solutions against vandalism.

As part of the MA programme, I have worked on assignments with multicultural groups that have exposed me to a wider understanding of brands and design strategies. For example, the Design Future

project on the future of interior design in children's hospitals enabled me to consider the importance of developing design thinking to communicate to that audience. This process needed us to think like a child, emphasising the need for design by and with people. This concept was also explored by Prof. Jeremy Myerson during the design futures seminar.

According to many speakers at the Design Futures seminar, the future of design is a perpetual re-thinking of the value of design at a triple bottom line level. My photographic studies of the Robin Hood Gardens in Blackwall, East London pin point the failure in adapting design to social changes and populations latent needs. On this point, the guest speaker Prof. Jeremy Myerson, called for "charting a changing paradigm in user centred design research process" which includes end users as active creators in the design decision making process. Designers should provide tools, processes and platforms that give businesses and end users, products and services for a wider use. Furthermore, a speech from Paula Zuccotti from Seymour Powell also recommended design as being "about making things better for people". Therefore, I have developed my research by working as a volunteer with local communities to identify the various needs and understanding of vandalism and the city decision making process.

Paola Loubli

MA Design & Branding Strategy

"By 2020, half the adult population will be aged over 50. So why do we continue to manufacture products and services aimed at young able-bodied consumers?" (Coleman, R, 2008)

As the ageing debate gains momentum, it is apparent that brands will need to adapt to new challenges.

The focus of my research is on wellness and beauty brands that currently tend to overlook the needs of the over 50's, (Mintel, 2009) due to our current youth obsessed society (Stroud, D, 2005).Beauty brands such as L'Oréal, Olay and Dove have started developing strategies to cater to older consumers, but this is the exception and not the rule whilst there is virtually no Wellness brand in the UK that does so.

One of the consequences of people living longer is the desire to continue living an active and independent lifestyle and ageing beautifully.Therefore, the aim of my research is to find the Wellness and Beauty requirements of an increasingly older generation using Design and Branding as the focal point, making older people more inclusive in a youth obsessed society whilst helping Wellness and Beauty brands adapt to this aging shift. In order to achieve this, I will be conducting qualitative and quantitative research methods such as literature reviews, looking at case studies such as OXO, conducting expert interviews, consumer focus groups and questionnaires, observing consumer behaviour and using cultural probes to gain new insights into the wellness and beauty requirements of older consumers.

One of the opportunities the MA in Brunel provided was to attend a workshop in St. Etienne in a multidisciplinary environment. Often designers are stereotyped as "too imaginative" or as "Blue Sky thinkers", and occasionally, this description is true. Working in a multidisciplinary workshop between designers and engineers in St. Etienne, was an unforgettable experience that taught me amongst many things, how to balance being creative but at the same time realistic, and the importance of working mutually with other disciplines in order to accomplish outstanding results.

This knowledge is indispensable for designers, to fulfill consumer requirements and create successful products or services.

Rita Marçal Ribeiro de Almeida
MA Design & Branding Strategy

Cutting Through Eco – Chaos
Understanding Consumer Sustainability Perceptions

With a tremendous use of raw materials, distribution networks, packaging needs and consumer demand, the Fast Moving Consumer Goods FMCG sector has a huge environmental footprint. As consumption increases, the political and financial pressure on FMCG firms to manage their footprint will be immense.

Understanding consumer perceptions and motivation is essential, as consumers have been identified as one of the most significant barriers to success in sustainability. Also, consumers frequently perceive companies to be either more or less sustainable than they really are. Often FMCG firms do not attempt to be more sustainable as they are unsure of consumer responses.

One of the biggest challenges in this area of research is that there is a huge disparity between what consumers say and what they do. "Eco-fatigue" might also have an impact on consumer response, as some people are tired of the sustainability movement. While some research has been conducted in this area, the issue of sustainability still remains quite abstract with reference to consumer behaviour.

Since consumer behaviour is hard to identify accurately, using different creative tools to check and crosscheck responses would be an ideal methodology. This project aims to design a research framework, which will help FMCG firms to get closer to the truth of things where straightforward market research has made little headway. By using a co-creative design platform (research tools, games and experiments) and involving extreme user groups, this project will develop a strategy to understand consumers.

As sustainability is a very real issue and will soon be an unavoidable need, this project could benefit both the FMCG firms that need to integrate sustainability as part of their agenda, as well as strategic design consultancies who need to help FMCG firms in designing sustainability agendas that are successful and strategies that are implementable.

A co-creative design approach was also used at 'Identities Materialized' (France), a workshop involving multidisciplinary teams of students from across the world collaborating to tackle the issue of protecting personal identities online.

From social to professional networking, we are increasingly reliant on online environments to facilitate our interactions. This poses the question- 'How can people effectively materialise their identities in these digital spaces?' The basic specifications were that our concept should consider "minimum disclosure of information", and "create user control and trust".

This open ended brief combined with the mixed cultural and educational backgrounds of participants prompted an organic co-creative method of using design, to conceptualise systems and solutions that would help people manage their multiple online identities. The outcome was an application that evaluates your personal online brand image and helps you to manage it.

During the Design Futures seminar at Brunel, speakers greatly influenced my design values and approach. In particular, Neil Tierney, who said 'the future of design is in proposing simple, effortless solutions to complex global challenges, rather than in sectors'.

Shikha Sabharwal
MA Design Strategy & Innovation

MSc - Smart Health
Enabling Lifestyles

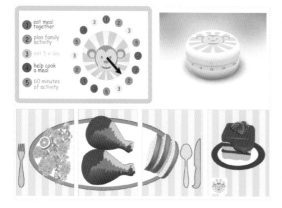

Our lifestyles are as individual as we are. Unfortunately certain groups of less able and older people are unable to live the way they want to due limited product choices. Our objective was to design products and systems that enabled people to live the way they want to. Our products range from encouraging people to become healthier, to drinking less and to become more independent.

Drinking Units

Over drinking is a major issue in UK. In 2009 the NHS spent £2.7 billion on health conditions caused by excessive drinking. The objective of the units bottle is to inform people of how many units they have consumed. The design concept redesigns the wine bottle packaging. The bottle is marked per unit as the user pours the wine into their glass. The label design also educates people to take care of their health.

MinYing Zhu

Cheeky Monkey Healthy Life Kit

The goal of the kit is to educate children through play about healthy eating and healthy cooking while encouraging them to be physically active. The kit will be distributed in schools to be used as an educational game. The kit consists of playing cards; each with a different food item and nutritional information. The objective of the playing cards is to build healthy meals using several different strategies. Children will play against their classmates coordinated by their teacher. A children's recipe book is included in the kit to allow children to actually cook the meals they are putting together with the playing cards. Bonus points can be earned by performing activities such as helping parents prepare a meal, eating 5 a day vegetable and fruits, and exercising.

Sabrina Tan

Sabrina Tan, MinYang Zhu
MSc Integrated Product Design

Zatoichi

There are about 200,000 people with acquired blindness in Japan. 33% of them could not cook after becoming blind. Zatoichi is a set of products that could help blind people cook by themselves. It consists of a hotplate, a stockpot and a special cookpen. The hotplate and pot solve the issues during the cooking process such as spillage, burning, temperature control, time control, through the heat insulating materials, Braille button, build-in speakers etc.For the food preparation, the cookpen could help select the food and freshness by identification sensors.

Ziyi Jin

Pill Reminder

Nowadays, increasing numbers of elderly people have memory loss. This project aims to remind elderly users to take their medicine on time and prevent them from medicine misuse. This medicine reminder system has two separate devices: Alarm Watch and Medicine Bottle Lock. The Alarm Watch is portable, therefore it could remind users to take pills on time and efficiently. Users could record what they would like each alarm to say with a unique reminder. Durable elastic bands means the Medicine Bottle Lock could hook to different shapes of bottles. The time release lock can be set to unlock at regular intervals, preventing users from taking pills repeatedly.

Minyan Shao

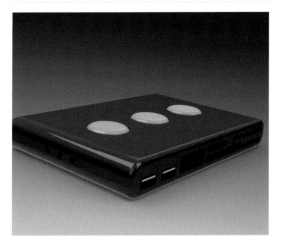

Health Hub

12.5% of the U.K's population has private healthcare. People are becoming increasingly health conscious, investing both time and money into their health. The Health Hub aims to promote living an active and healthy lifestyle. By monitoring their health regularly and sharing this data with their healthcare provider, they will in turn receive reduced insurance premiums.

Tom Gale

Minyan Shao, Ziyi Jin, Tom Gale
MSc Integrated Product Design

If we were to reflect on the last 10 years in terms of design we would talk about innovation, sustainability, embracing technology…but more importantly, the acceptance of the changing nature of design. Design is now seen as a tool for promoting change, and it is this responsibility that we as a group, have decided to focus on. How will we live in 2018? This question represents our group's design intentions, it evolved from the idea of designing for the future home, meeting the needs of the future consumer, considering technological, economical, environmental and social issues. However, instead of designing solutions for tomorrow, we need solutions that are feasible today, we recognised the need for forward thinking, but not futuristic thinking, the excitement about what we can do has faded, and the focus is now on how it can work for us.

E-Sensory Shopping
Sik Choo's proposed design solution targets the aging population and aims to integrate an 'e-grocery' service within shared dwellings. It features a quick and easy-to-use website that creates an 'e-sensory' shopping experience using innovative, interactive features designed specifically for working and retired consumers. The design adopts a holistic approach to the consumer shopping experience, and sustainable design strategies have been applied throughout. Our intent is to promote a sustainable and healthy lifestyle for elderly people.
Sik Choo Lim

Pick Your Own Produce
Richard's project explores social innovation as a means of problem solving to address food management and

Sik Choo Lim, Richard Archer
MSc Integrated Product Design

health care issues. The proposed concept is the development of a social, educational environment promoting healthy, sustainable urban living ideals that highlight the functional properties of food. Loosely based upon the traditional producer-consumer market model, the store grows produce on site and sources from local allotments, farms and individuals within the community, allowing the customer to pick produce "straight from the ground it's grown in" within the store itself. The aim is to develop a model that improves food security by integrating urban agricultural practice, educating consumers and stimulating change supporting shifting consumer trends.

Grow At Home
As more and more people are becoming aware of the environmental impact of food transportation, the demand for alternative, more sustainable sources of fresh produce is increasing. The rise in popularity of allotments is an example of this trend at a community level, and vertical gardens and high-rise city farms are being developed as commercial alternatives. Mark aims to achieve a solution with the 'grow at home' project. This product provides the optimum growing conditions for fruit and vegetables indoors, and a service whereby users will have constant access to information and advice. The connection will be made via your home Internet and provide access to a community of experts and novices.

Mark Ayres

Global Meter
Leonard's project involves the design of a smart meter that addresses the need to reduce energy and water consumption through behaviour change. The 'global meter' attempts to engage users on an emotional level by displaying the feedback through a variety of simulated environments that portray the natural world. These environments adapt and evolve according to the user's consumption of energy and water. The aim is to make the user more aware of their impact on the environment and to encourage more efficient use of products within the home.

Leonard Marti

Cooling Fruit Bowl
Today, in the U.K we throw away one third of the food we purchase, almost half is salad and one quarter is fruit. Much of this wasted food could have been eaten if it had been stored properly; it is a known fact that fruit and vegetables last longer if they are kept cold. Hiral's proposed solution addresses food storage in the design of a ceramic bowl with passive cooling. The cooling effect is created through evaporation requiring only water and sand. This cooling fruit bowl features a transparent cover that maintains the required atmospheric conditions whilst allowing the contents to be viewed by the user.

Hiral Desai

Mark Ayres, Leonard Marti, Hiral Desai
MSc Integrated Product Design

MSc - Public Space
Transforming spaces into places

We believe that public space should be a place for everyone and that a place should not be defined by its designer, but by its user. Currently many public spaces are impersonal with little thought into the facilities offered for the people who use it. If local people do not feel connected to a place it decays and social interaction around the place is lost. Our aim is to create engaging places; to increase the enjoyment people have in those spaces; or to add something to existing locations in order to encourage a positive response to that space where people interact with the environment and with each other.

London is the largest city in Europe, with a dramatic variation of people from all ages and cultures offering a huge amount of design opportunities. Our aim is to use design research and design thinking to tackle a variety of social issues within public spaces in London. After conducting secondary research and ethnographic studies, a range of stakeholders were interviewed. These included an award winning architect in the field of urban design, a landscape architect from the local council, and an academic on regional planning. We consolidated our research during group meetings into a strategic overview with an overall vision of transforming public space into public places. This has led to a number of individual projects.

Social Interaction and Street Furniture Systems
This project aimed to increase social interaction by installation of street furniture. It is based on creating an environment and furniture system which is arranged in a way to encourage people to stop and have a look.

Shruti Shah, Emily Calladine
MSc Integrated Product Design

The furniture should nurture opportunities for people to sit and strike up a conversation; they always say that "great ideas emerge when people talk to each other".

Shruti Shah

Cigarette Litter
The aim was to reduce cigarette litter on the streets of London. Working with smokers in order to engage with the culture and rituals of smoking resulted in a proposal for a combined cigarette case and personal ash tray for women that was also a personalisable high-end accessory.

Emily Calladine

Softening Barriers
Barriers are often imposing, authoritarian objects with little sense of place. The Hackney Tiles project was inspired by the utopian principles of place-making and participatory design, creating a community design project working with local people and heritage.

Rich Young

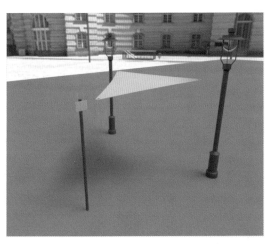

Social Interaction and Street Culture
The aim was to encourage social interaction through entertainment by understanding all the existing situations that bring people together, like public art, music and theatre. The creation of friendly environments and comfortable street spaces will convert a city into a more human and enjoyable living place.

Jorge Álvarez

Redefining Waiting Points
Looking at new ways of bringing people together; this is a high-tech, self-sustaining bus shelter called "Nimbus". Resembling the clouds in terms of design, shape, materials and lighting it helps in keeping people relaxed and promotes social interaction. Turning people's unavoidable, often daily, waiting time into a whole new experience.

Thelma Kalentzoti

Rich Young, Jorge Álvarez, Themla Kalenztzoti
MSc Integrated Product Design

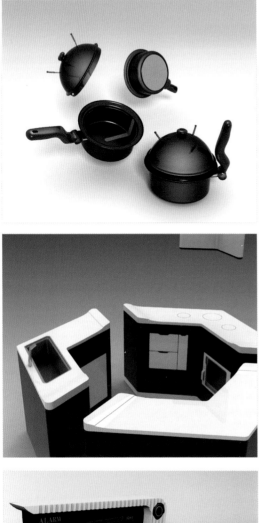

Through questionnaire-based primary research, people stressed that time is the biggest barrier for food preparation, cooking and cleaning. Monitoring the cooker and controlling the temperature and cooking times is also difficult. TopoT is a multifunctional pan which, with its lid, provides a unique and ingenious solution for temperature indication using a sensing band inside the pot. The lid also functions as the washing bowl for preparing food and by placing the lid on its extendable feet acts as a second serving dish. It simplifies cooking and saves time. With additional functions such as the foldable handle for saving storage space and the special pouring edge of the pot for drip free cooking, TopoT fits a contemporary lifestyle - convenient, useful and effective.

Ding Wang

In our contemporary society, cooking is experiencing a renaissance period and being rediscovered as an everyday entertainment activity. Simultaneously, governments and food manufacturers are promoting healthy diets through cooking. The project consists of the design and development of a set of kitchen units, which could promote cooking by improving the efficiency, convenience and hygiene of a kitchen environment. The design proposal is intended for individuals who are willing to cook but simply do not have the time to. It incorporates emerging kitchen trends where the essential units are integrated within living spaces. The final modular form was the result of combining user movement patterns and essential features into space saving units. The entire system consists of three modular units to define the different zones in a kitchen; HOT, COLD and SOCIAL workstations.

Lee Hyun Dong

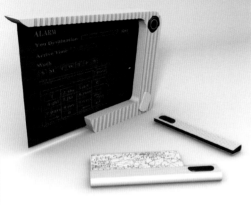

The well-being of a person is characterised by their quality of life. Research shows that 33% of commuters are regularly late for work due to traffic and travel problems. This design aims to improve this problem, and at the same time improve the quality of people's home life, making commuters feel happy and light hearted. The product has two parts; the home unit provides an alarm clock function which is linked to an online traffic information service to compensate for travel conditions. The portable unit is also linked to real time travel information as well as transmitting location information to the home unit to provide information and reassurance to people's families.

Ying Liu

Ding Wang, Lee Hyun Dong, Ying Liu
MSc Integrated Product Design

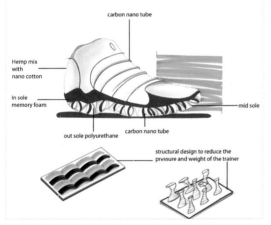

The world is fast-paced and driven by work-based technology. High-stress work frequently makes people ignore the affect of poor working conditions on their health. Increasing awareness of individual's working wellbeing helps to improve health and work efficiency. The conceptual product focuses on the wellbeing of its users. It encourages people to get out of the mess and poor air quality of many workplaces, finding healthier, comfortable working environments. Unlike the limited portability of existing laptops etc. this work station is small enough to put in a pocket. It adopts projection and multi–touch technology, enabling people to interact with the content stored in the device. The screen can be defined as any physical surface, such as magazine, folder, newspaper etc. It can also be used as a normal projector to cater for multi–person viewing.

Bo Peng

Designing comfortable and safe trainers for basketball players is essential for their well-being. Utilising developments in nanotechnology provides opportunities to reduce the shoe weight, managing sweat and moisture and minimising the pressure that is transmitted through the sole of the foot. Ankle injuries which are common amoungst basketball players should be significantly reduced through the use of carbon nanotubes in a new composite sole structure.

Saba Eshragu

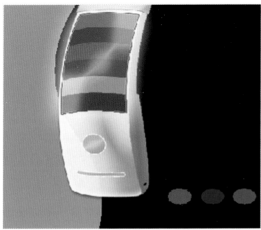

In modern society young people like to listen to music anytime or anywhere. However, using MP3 players at high volumes can permanently damage people's hearing. This health problem is addressed by this concept with four main features: a listening-time limit, visual indication of volume, bluetooth and combining the MP3 player with the headphones. The key function of the new headphone-MP3 players is the listening-time feature. An OLED display in the headband displays colours responding to each 10 minutes of listening-time. At the maximum listening time of 60 minutes, the volume will fade. A second function of the visual indication is to powerfully indicate the safe listening whatever the ambient volume of the environment. A healthy listening volume is less than 80 Decibels. Therefore 60 Decibels for a maximum 60 minutes is an important design feature. Bluetooth allows the product to be used in conjunction with mobile phones and for downloads and the integration of MP3 player within the product makes this suitable for active pursuits.

Yanjiao Wang

Bo Peng, Saba Eshragu, Yanjiao Wang
MSc Integrated Product Design

virtual innovation

 Digital, multimedia, online
and new media
based concepts

In the last ten years, multimedia and
internet technologies have become an
essential part of everyday life. This digital
era has altered our social behaviour,
but is still relatively unexplored, giving
rise to new design opportunities.
Rapid interaction and communication
is defined by speed, making our lives
and the concepts within this chapter
driven by the fourth-dimension - time.

iCare for Autism
Enhancing the relationship between carer and autistic child

Care profiles are paper based systems created for autistic children to communicate vital information to all those involved with their care.

iCare for Autism is an iPhone app based on profiling systems used by professional carers. The parent creates a profile, other carers use, edit and update it. iCare for Autism does everything paper based care profiles do, but harnesses the power of mobile platforms, automatically linking pages of the profile to relevant online information.

Profiles contain recipes of a child's favourite meals based on specific dietary requirements. Carers can find the child's favourite places on a map, avoid any disliked locations, and find their way to the locations of important appointments. There is an updatable schedule of expected behaviours as a reference for therapists. Carers can discover important information about medication the child is using, including side effects and administration. Profiles can be shared wirelessly with employers, colleagues and teachers. Profiles can also be emailed to other platforms.

Matthew Debnam
Product Design Engineering BSc

The matching or 'suitability' of computer spatial input devices to application software is not something that has been strongly considered or evaluated outside the niche of video games. The ability to rate devices on their suitability for different applications provides a method for manufacturers and developers to improve on their products and use the ratings as a promotional tool.

Through device testing utilising specially developed software tests, the system evaluates the device data and provides a suitability score in six different software categories. Scores are presented in a rating format out of ten possible scores, which also translate into a ten star system. The device scores identified can then aid in marketing the device, or be used for development by device manufacturers. Consumers can benefit from the system as it provides an unbiased and accurate way of ensuring that they can choose the device most suited to their needs.

Ben Curnow

Industrial Design & Technology BA

Marvel Comic Book Guide

User-interface to enhance and improve the experience of collecting comics

Comic book collecting has become a thriving business on the back of comic book films spawning a new generation of collectors. This application will help engage this audience through the use of modern technology as well as enhancing the experience of veteran collectors.

The USP of this approach is the visual element, and the increased functionality and usability that comes with having the actual comic book cover in front of you when looking for a specific comic. This vastly improves on the current methods of keeping track of comic book collections, which mainly use lists and very static, inflexible, text databases.

Portability of comic collection information is another vital part of this application. Having detailed, up-to-date and visual information is useless unless it is accessible whenever and wherever you need it. To further the appeal of this application an extra feature is the search function which enables you to find all work produced by your favourite artist or all appearances of your favourite character.

Andrew Morley
Industrial Design BSc

Also on p.150

A pollen goes on an adventure to find the perfect flower

A project focusing on pollination which aims to create a funny, friendly short animation that shows the life of a pollen grain and its journey to pollinate. The idea was to show something very small and how scale could be used to portray their small world.

Movies, such as 'A bug's life' were a particular inspiration, as they portray an infinitesimally vast world, but inhabited with empathetic creatures with human characteristics.

The animation is about a pollen grain, that goes on a dangerous adventure to find the perfect flower to pollinate with, along the way the viewer will see alternative pollination methods. The aim to create the animation in a distinctive art style, that was engaging for audiences, especially younger children who will find this educational, but also fun to watch rather than a documentary on pollination, which may be less appealing.

Hena Bhatti
Multimedia Technology & Design BSc

Pagani Zonda R Commercial
A fully 3D commercial for the Pagani Zonda R supercar

A project to model and animate a Pagani Zonda car and to create a short television commercial from it aimed at glamorising the Pagani brand using an original style. The outside and inside of the car were modelled from scratch using 3D Studio Max and several environments were created to place it in. It was then animated and rendered out as part of a commercial for the car. Taking inspiration from Italian graphic design and cinematography to create a piece which is set in Milan and at the Palmach Museum in Israel. A 20-page leaflet was also produced filled with still renders from the animation.

Hugh Wyeth
Multimedia Technology & Design BSc

Also on p.294

Bugzi.org.uk
Online resource for the Bugzi wheelchair

Each year in the UK around 1000 children are born with disabilities that seriously affect their mobility.

The Bugzi wheelchair enables children aged 12 months to 5 years to experience independent mobility for the first time, to explore their environment and to develop spatial awareness and social skills.

Bugzi.org.uk is a website designed to inform parents and occupational therapists about the benefits of the Bugzi wheelchair. The website includes case studies and user stories alongside user manuals for a comprehensive resource about the product.

Lynne Peacock
Multimedia Design & Technology BSc

Currently charities do not have enough support, money, or resources to adequately utilise the web as a fundraising medium (setting up and running a fundraising website). Most currently available open-source solutions are either too complicated and specialised for non-developers to grasp, or the available free templates are geared towards e-commerce and brochure-style websites. Neither fully meet the needs of a fundraising organisation. The basis of this project was to create a Web application for fundraising organisations/individuals to better utilise the web. The British Association for Adoption and Fostering (BAAF) were in need of a microsite to house their fundraising content and promotion. Based on discussions with them a microsite was designed, based on requirements to deal with the current fundraising section which was suffering from "content overload". This also involved creating an easy to use web-based Content Management System for the population and management of the microsite. This also allows the fundraising Team to update the website themselves.

Theresa Pert
Multimedia Design & Technology BSc

Digital Media Theatre Performance
A live theatre performance with interactive multimedia installation elements

A short live theatre performance with interactive multimedia installation elements such as: touch sensors, camera motion detection and multiple video projection screens. This performance is a personal experiment to combine multimedia with a previous study in acting in a seamless and meaningful way. This experiment tests the level of integration and examines the impact in our digital and visual driven era. The outcomes will provide a unique experience that may be applied in other forms such as museums, galleries or festival multimedia installations.

Considerations include: Installation - the physical mapping of the equipment (camera, sensors and projectors) in the space and its' smooth functionality; the Play's style, aesthetics and meaningfulness; and Human Computer Interaction - the impact this experience is going to have on the visitor, theatre industry and actors.

The work raises the question: is digital technology changing theatre from group to individual profession, more "one man show" and the "hyper-actor" who can manage everything ?

Calliope Georgousi
Multimedia Technology & Design BSc

The idea of virtual reality gaming is not without creative exploration, however this project aimed to explore some of the more realistic possible features and methods of execution.

The idea was that a purpose built environemnt would use state of the art motion capture technology combined with a hydraulic platform which would rise from the ground and create a physical boundary or obstacle in place of the virtual one seen by the user through the visor or VR helmet.

This idea combines virtual reality with haptic feedback systems and integrates the two in a way which is believable, contextual and quite easily possible in the near future.

The project consists of a 3D action sequence demonstrating the technical side of the project within a video exert of a fictional documentary with possible expansion into the details and functionality of a physical proxy VR system.

James Littek
Broadcast Media (Design & Technology) BSc

Rosie - A Short Film

A short animation about Rosie, a hungry dog

A 3D animated short film about Rosie the dog and her search for food. Aimed at being an entertaining, charming and technically competent short film. Several characters and environments were modelled from scratch for the animation, which is set in the south of France on a lazy summer afternoon.

Having been woken up from a dream about eating lots of food, Rosie goes off searching for something to eat. What started out as a simple task ends in a small adventure as Rosie nearly gets eaten herself! The story was inspired by Pixar's own short films as well as French animations like "Les Triplettes de Belleville".

Hugh Wyeth

Multimedia Technology & Design BSc

Also on p.288

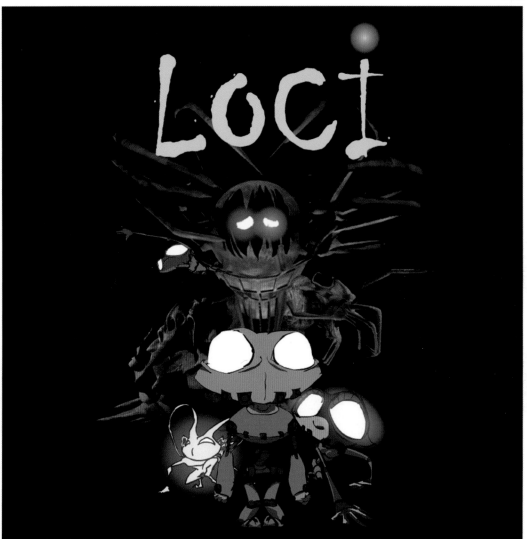

Loci is a short film with an unconventional story, brought to life through highly stylised 2D and 3D composite animation. The story and the plot are distinctly divided into the memories of the protagonist and the present moment, allowing for twists that may not be possible with more linear storylines. The setting and characters are part of a cathartic and compelling world, where the co-existence of 2D and 3D components is more than just a stylistic choice.

Various positively aligned characters are fleshed out in colourful and expressive Flash animations, while the antagonists and the cold, unforgiving world they live in, are all modelled using 3DS max. All components are then composited in After Effects. The end result is a atmospheric animation that is all the more captivating due to the juxtaposition of contrasting mediums. Loci offers an alternative approach to modern animation that enables animators with a lack of resources, but no lack of ambitions, to create pieces that garner people's interest.

David Christensen
Multimedia Technology & Design BSc

Moon Fox Games

A website to play and create your own games

A final year project to create a website where people can create their own unique Flash games, as well as browse through and play all of the games that have been created.

The game creator produces platform games, and users design the layout of the game, choose the objects within the game (selecting their type and design from a menu), as well as the design of their game character. The game creator application is designed to be easy to use, incorporating a drag and drop system to design the game layout, so users do not need to do any coding and almost anyone can use it. The overiding goal was that each game should be really personalised and individual to the maker.

The product's target audience is aged from around 13 to 25. Many young people enjoy playing games online, so a website where they can easily create their very own games as well as play them would be really appealing. There are a few existing game creator websites, but this website stems not only from thorough research into useability but also into what users want to create a site everyone will enjoy using.

Heather Roberts
Multimedia Technology & Design BSc

In live musical performances of electronic music, the separation of musician and VJ (or 'visual jockey', responsible for projection of visuals) often leads to arbitrary, bland or uncomplimentary visuals. Idiron AV aims to bridge the gap between two multimedia disciplines through the development of a bespoke interactive audio/visual system for live projection of sophisticated visuals that are symbiotic to the musical performance itself. Essentially a conglomeration of creative digital technologies and disciplines, it can be catagorised into three core areas;

1) The artistic creation of visual elements through CGI and manipulated HD footage, and deconstruction of musical compositions into component motifs and elements.

2) The development of patches and code to translate musical notation and audio properties into easily networked real-time data streams that work flexibly with the functionality of VJ software.

3) Removal of all traditional interaction in favour of intuitive custom hands-on control with ergonomic multimedia devices.

Gilbert Sinnott
Multimedia Technology & Design BSc

2010: The Year of the Smart Meter
Who will really benefit?

With stuttering climate talks, an underachieving 'Hopenhagen' conference and a struggling economy, future advancement looks bleak. Governments, their hands forced by public pressure have turned their focus to developing a Smart Meter strategy, in an attempt to answer the ever-impending question of how to cut carbon emissions? For years there has been speculation surrounding the adoption of Smart Meter initiatives, which seemed like a campaign redolent of feigning politics. 2010, however, brings fresh vigour to a pursuit that could see initiatives realised in the imminent future.

The aftermath of the disappointing meeting in Copenhagen has seen governing officials put full faith in smart meters to answer the questions left unsolved during the Climate Change summit in December, 2009. The realisation of policies supporting the adoption of a smart meter is not just confined to the UK. President Obama and the US government have proposed a $4.5 billion subsidisation to stimulate a national rollout of smart meters. Across the European Union politicians are pushing for legislation that will see the deployment of smart meters into 80% of homes and businesses by 2020. The Smart Meter buzz has stretched to emerging markets such as China and India, both looking to this as a method to improve their international environmental prestige.

On the surface, the policies look strong and, although scepticism is prevalent, there is a definitive argument in support of this world wide initiative coupled with an unmistakable need for change. Smart Meters, consequently, seem to propose a convenient answer to a riddle that has puzzled global climate change pioneers for the past decade. However, is this new found enthusiasm for electronic utility monitoring really the solution to a sensitive and complex problem? Or perhaps more importantly who is going to see the real benefit?

The Householder
To the eyes of a willing consumer, the smart meter may seem like a blessing. The ability to constantly monitor the home's electricity usage in real-time, seems undoubtedly beneficial.

The perceived core aim of the Smart Meter Scheme is to save the consumer money on their energy bills and increase the transparency of the utility provider-customer dyad, subsequently shifting more control

and flexibility to the user. At least, that is the plan.

Early claims from the Department for Energy and Climate Change (DECC) stated householders could save in excess of 10 per cent on their energy bills, however recent publications show that this may have been an embarrassing over-estimate. The DECC claims officials calculated the actual saving to be £28 per year by 2020, which is dramatically lower than the £100 previously suggested.

The figures from the DECC publications also estimate each Smart Meter to cost £340. Unavoidably, it seems that the householder will incur this charge from the utility provider, either as a lump sum, or increase. The underlying assumptions of this scheme become increasingly dubious when retrospectively considering a 'plan' that has been in deliberation for almost a decade, and could suggest that the requirements of the householder were left out of the equation, for the most part.

The Energy Industry
Predictably first in line will be energy utility companies who are set to see improvements across all lines of business. The traditional paradigm that perplexed many and loomed over the industry has ostensibly lost its relevance. It was once presumed that the more energy customers consume, the higher the profits for the provider. This posed an intriguing paradox as theoretically Smart Meters encourage lower levels of energy consumption, ultimately translating into lower profits for these providers. In spite of this, utility companies remain keen to see the policies passed.

The answer is simple: the potential of this scheme for the industry is much more complex and infinitely more fruitful than at first glance. For instance, the maintenance and man-hours needed to check meters at homes across the UK will be eradicated, equating to £2.66 billion in savings alone. The total supplier benefits amount to £6 billion. This huge cost saving incentive smashes the paradox of previous preconceptions that, otherwise, could have seen the utility industry revolt against the use of smart meters.

The "centralised communications model" has seen the UK's leading telecommunication giants, Vodafone, O$_2$ and BT battling to win contracts, said to be worth billions. The smart meters will use the network coverage, provided by the 'telecom' company, to connect the household to the utility supplier. The utility companies may become vulnerable in this scenario as it removes much of their control, and creates a 'middle-man' business model between themselves and their customers; resulting in low risk-high reward, business potential for the telecom giants in the 'middle.'

The Secret Industry
Smart meters bring an exciting, yet alarming opportunity with the birth of a new generation of consumer-intrusive technology. Companies providing your electricity can identify each appliance in your home, when you use them, and as a result build a database of knowledge and a marketing arsenal that could change the way we live.

Each electronic appliance in your home draws a unique amount of power and current from the mains, making each product distinguishable. ISE, a sustainable energy company, have developed technology which uses patented algorithms to 'teach' the meter about your home and, if utilised correctly, could be an extremely powerful and remunerative tool for the 'owners' of the technology, and this could lead to further exploitation of the consumer.

The people behind the UK governments ActOnCO2 campaign, AMEE, try to paint a more acceptable picture. AMEE say they will utilise this technology as part of a comprehensive system that produces an open database where consumers could look up a model of product and find out how much energy it really uses, in practice, based on real data from users (as opposed to what the manufacturers claim) and compare products based on energy usage. This would provide the consumer with a remarkable way of avoiding marketing jargon. Nevertheless, this could turn out to be in parenthesis to the real benefits of this breakthrough. The licensing of this technology and the database it produces will create a new industry worth billions; and the consumer, more likely than not, will be unaware of its very existence.

Seeds of Change, Sowed by Change
Although it is debatable who will see the 'real' benefit, if quantified financially, one concurrent theme is that this is a step in the right direction regarding cutting carbon emissions. The short term will see the utility and telecommunication companies happiest, with

the householder's control and potential for personal change increasing. As the industry evolves, long-term benefits will allow the advancement of wider policy goals and the deployment of smarter, more effective, technologies.

Due to the myopic and bureaucratic nature of government the effectiveness of this scheme is questionable. In the UK, the Labour government's term of office came to an end in the 2010 election. In light of this, its green policies may only be a desperate final attempt to save face of an administration bowing out, to reflect on what was a capricious 13 years in Government, however no one can be sure. It is, however, incontrovertible that the current energy industry does need to change, and although the motives and reasoning behind smart meters may be ambiguous, the goal of affecting climate change will be one step closer with the evolution of a decadent industry. These schemes should plant the seed for future progress and attempt to create a more sustainable vista regarding energy use in the future. Although there are varying degrees of enthusiasm regarding the scheme, the politicians and 'powers that be' seem certain and committed, that this is the right move to yield the highest benefits.

In theory, the 'climate' should be the key stakeholder in this scheme, yet even with the blatant virtue lying with other parties, it seems to be a step forward to a 'greener' future, even if the environmental consequences are a coincidental by-product of a financially lucrative operation.

by Mitch Neofytou
Product Designer

Can Pac-Man Make You Cry?
Narrative interface and design

"Aren't you a bit old for games?" I've had a couple of run-ins with this criticism before. It usually preceded Daily Mail dogma on how Mario was an allegory to paedophilia and a risk to your kids. The question was sneered at me across the dinner table by a woman of that certain age. On previous occasions my confidence had waned and I failed to make my point. This time I was ready. I would disregard proper dining decorum, leave the room and begin a witty but careful analysis on the beauty of games.

I would celebrate games' intuitive and challenging designs. I would applaud their rich and immersive worlds and their ability to move players to tears with their interactive narratives. I would explain how the games industry is experiencing a renaissance and how games could be at the turning point of transforming into art. Then finally, from under the table I would pull out a carefully illustrated pie chart (expertly mounted on foam board), visually communicating how much more money video games are making in comparison to the film industry. This would be my final blow. A bow. Applause. Exit stage left. But proper dining decorum refused to disappear and all I could manage was a submissive "Yeah. I guess I am".

Traditional media paints an ugly picture of video games. By paint, I mean spray sensationalistic vitriol. Searing vitriol that fingers video games for many of the problems in society: teenage angst, bad parenting, diabetes etc. But the degradation of emerging or differential art forms has been a perpetual transgression of the scared and confused for centuries. "A pastime of illiterate wretched creatures who are stupefied by their daily jobs, a machine of mindlessness and dissolution." The French novelist George Duhamel was not characterising video games but lamenting cinema nearly 80 years ago.

There is a loud majority of games that do promote a mindless stereotype, exploiting a generic wish fulfilment found in many forms of popular media. Many games are stuck in the realm of the teenage boy; lusting over big guns and bigger boobs. Every year we are bestowed by hundreds of impossibly macho space marines who have seem to have just graduated from the overly-dramatic-dialogue-with-complementary-pensive-look school. But, however exaggerated and implausible these quasi characters are, they suck us into their world.

Games, more than any other medium, can be utterly enveloping. There isn't a better example of this than the massively successful World of Warcraft. The game snares players so successfully that the developers must either be channelling demonic powers or experimental psychologists that have demonic powers. Players are so compelled to play that they will not leave their computers for days on end. World of Warcraft players would rather wear nappies than leave their preferred reality for a virtual second. What are the primordial drivers, pushing people to such unhygienic heights?

Mammals. It's because we are mammals. We love to play and it's hard wired into our brains. In his book, the Art of Computer Game Design, Chris Crawford talks about the evolutionary precursors to playing games. How lion cubs fight and grapple with each other, pounce on butterflies and generally look photogenic. We say the cubs are playing a game, and "aww look at the cute kitty having care-free fun!" No, this is deadly serious. They are not care-free animals, these are hunters in training. They play games to test out their skills in a safe environment. And that's what games are: representations of reality. We interact with their conflict in a safe arena. Maybe instead of loving to play games, we love to learn. This idea of representation drives many aspects found in games. They allow us a safe realm to release our anger on society. They can fulfil our fantasies and facilitate the removal of us from ourselves. Games can acknowledge our efforts as we paint our own personalities into them. Great games allow us to explore and expose our own character and be rewarded for it.

Art, to me, is communication. Of ideas, of stories. Communication so powerful it is beautiful. The first narratives were used around campfires. Today artists use a vast array of media to communicate their ideas, their stories. And these media have been incredibly effective in reaching out to huge numbers of people. How many people have been affected by Star Wars or moved by a Picasso painting. Chris Crawford explains that when he is doing one of his lectures he is being incredibly efficient; hundreds of people get to hear him and learn from his ideas. Though if you had a one to one conversation with him, how much more would you learn? You would have the ability to ask questions and interact. The quality of the information would far greater and much more specific. This is the exceptional nature of video games, being able to be part of the story, to engage emotionally with the fictional world. Though the tether between fact and this fiction might be one of the main repulsions of many non gamers; the physical connection is so alien that it's terrifying.

As I take aim on my hapless target, the wind whistles through the barrel of my cold gun. I squeeze the trigger; I don't blink. Though I'm not really squeezing any trigger, I've pushed a half pence plastic button. There is no need for this corny aimless description. After the shot, I feel a strange pity for the motor in my joypad that valiantly tries to vibrate my hands into emotional ecstasy and early arthritis. It's at this point I begin to see the deep dark crack of a problem. The victorious trump card of this new medium is its interactivity, but the physical input of the interaction is one of video games' biggest stumbling blocks.

Currently, the mental stress enjoyed by the cognitive side of gaming heavily contrasts with the woeful physical actions of actually playing the game. What is the tactile relationship between jumping and hitting the space bar? It's unrealistic and overwhelmingly mediocre. This disconnect affects the inexperienced gamer the most. The majority of gamers have had years of experience, learning the lexicon of gameplay. The disconnect is now so expected it isn't jarring. Though new gamers have an experience debt causing them to be overwhelmed by the performance required. The Wii currently tries to straddle the disconnect, allowing the player to be physically engaged in the action. Though the Wii falls foul of a fundamental game design problem: it isn't seamless, the controls aren't consistent or responsive. Soon, as the controls fail, the suspension on my disbelief is lifted and I'm immediately transported from the lush fields of Hyrul back to my stained sofa, where I seem to be, from an outsider's point of view, furiously waving a TV remote. And it is a TV remote, but that of course is an intentional act of living room doppelgangery; which has proven to be incredibly successful. The Wii's competitors, with their devil like horns and their overpowering plastic acne, are too terrifying to even approach for someone like my mum; but that white TV remote is understandable. The Wii has finally made a connection with people that would never usually play games. Even with the control issues getting more people to play games is great, right? Unfortunately the games that this new market is presenting are woefully unrepresentative of the true potential of games. They're playing party games and bowling. From this perspective they're still seen as toys not as a respected art form.

The game industry is beginning to feel the pressure to aspire to the pretentious heights of other mediums, though there is no need for games to have such low self-esteem. I may have lambasted the more visceral games, but the artistic skill and engineering precision needed to create them is truly phenomenal. The question if video games have any value is erroneous, It's better to ask if the question itself has any value. All popular art forms are built on a premise of entertainment, a distraction from the world. Video games have the potential to be the greatest procrastination tool, totally engaging the user on every level of their consciousness. But this is just the beginning, games are so young that in terms of cinema they've just added sound. They still have to go through a difficult adolescence, full of awkward firsts and smelling of too much body spray. With a little development however, video games have all of the potential to become an all encompassing and inclusive medium for delivering diversion to a wide variety of procrastinators not just the current niche.

By Tom Wakeling

The Forecast is... Cloudy...

The Internet is an evolving entity, and how we use and consume it is constantly changing. However beyond the day-to-day development, what do we need to consider as businesses, individuals and citizens of the Internet, when it comes to defining the evolution of the net as we move into a cloud computing era?

Later this year marks the 20th anniversary of the world wide web although the Internet can trace its history back much further, to the 1960s. We have seen the web mature during this time, from its early incarnation as a series of read-only, static pages and images, to a dynamic, social and more collaborative environment.

Of course, now there are many varying purposes for the web. We use it for communicating, entertaining, socialising and debating. It is a crucial tool used by individuals to get their views across, by businesses to trade and by everyone to find information.

Driving the web's ability to push into more and more areas of our lives has been the gradual increase in bandwidth and the ability of websites to utilise this capacity. Twenty years ago YouTube would never have been possible, yet today it has become one of the most popular destinations online.

The Internet has and will become more ubiquitous. As it becomes more integrated with everyday life, we will start to see less of a distinction between off and on line. It has become widely recognised that the Internet is a utility alongside water, electricity, oil and gas.

The always-on Internet has meant that as individuals we have embedded it into our everyday lives. Google has become the de facto first port of call for everything; tweets and status updates are made constantly; and we rely on instant messaging and email to keep in touch. It is not surprising that we want to take this world with us on the go.

You and I expect that we have access to our data everywhere we go. It seems archaic that we should only be able to access emails from one computer, or not see the latest updates from our social networks whilst out and about.

This demand for access everywhere has been a contributing factor in the rise of the 'cloud', the concept of computing software and hardware as a service. Now, this is not a particularly new idea: for instance web-based email has been around for many years. What is new is the push to move more and more of our data online.

Virtually every piece of software available as a desktop application can now be found online, as a web application, often for free. There are versions of photo editing tools, office suites, email systems, project management tools, bookkeeping... the list is endless. All run in the Internet browser, which to some has become the most important piece of their computer software.

The most successful of these systems give you the right tools for access on the go. You probably would not want to create your next Photoshop masterpiece on your iPhone, but you probably will want to check some quick details in a spreadsheet, or see progress on the latest project.

One of the reasons that Adobe's Flash technology has fallen out of favour is that it is designed to deliver the same, identical, experience to every browser and every device. In the app-generation, we are expecting a customised experience depending on the method we use to access the service. This is reflected in the success of Apple's App Store for the iPhone, and is the reason why other mobile operating system makers are so eager to create their own.

The cost of mobile handsets keeps falling, and hopefully this will mean they can be a massive force for good in some of the world's least developed countries. With little fixed-line and power infrastructure, mobile technologies will be the best way to get some of the poorest inhabitants of Earth online, to deliver the educational, financial and health benefits that this brings.

Again, the cloud will be instrumental in this – as infrastructure in data-centres thousands of miles away can be accessed through low-cost, low-power, mobile devices. Of course, there are challenges here for designers, both in terms of the design of a new generation of frugal and environmental mobile phones with all the features of our current Internet-enabled smartphones, and also for the designers and developers of the services that will run on them.

This audience may not have previously used a desktop

computer, so we have to rethink all of the interface assumptions we make as a result.

However, much as the cloud can remove some of the entrance barriers to software, knowledge and resources, it also has some serious questions to answer. Are we ceding responsibility for this data to the right people? And are we always checking how it might be used?

Privacy is of course a major area of contention as we increasingly move our personal lives, business data and memories into the cloud. Precisely who has access to our data, how it will be used and even who ultimately owns it are all questions that should be asked. Perhaps these are the responsibility of individuals as they sign up to services, but how many of us ever read software terms?

Our company makes extensive use of cloud and managed web services, for hosting, accounting, email, documents and project management. In some cases we have chosen based on cost (free!), in others because it is the best way of making sure the data is accessible to the whole team. We are even developing our own web-based software offering, so we are firmly in the cloud.

But what happens when you want to move to another provider? How do you move your data?

Essentially, as computing power and software becomes more and more commoditised, your data becomes the valuable item. How do we ensure that as software and data storage is centralised, individuals retain rights and access to their data and can get this data in a manner that can be migrated to other providers?

Of equal importance is whether all data is created equal. The issue of net neutrality, the idea that all data should be transported through the Internet's infrastructure with equal priority, is bound to come under further pressure as more and more services move to the cloud.

If the Googles of the world become too powerful we are in danger of seeing control of our data and the way it is delivered being ceded to one organisation. This fundamentally clashes with the founding principle that the Internet, the web and the other services that run upon it, are decentralised and that there is no single source of all data.

Got something to add? Comment online at www.nakedcreativity.co.uk/cloudy

By Jordan Chitty

Jordan is Creative Director at Naked Creativity, the branding, graphic design and website development agency he established after graduating from Brunel in 2007.

Active Together
Future design concepts for Kellogg's

In 2020 it is projected that Kellogg's will have expanded their traditional family brand to increase focus on social wellbeing within local communities. Active Together outlines the potential to build on existing opportunities to meet together as a community, in order to enhance our day to day activities.

Reducing the social barriers lets others know when you are next active, the device raises the awareness of unplanned or coincidental activities that people share together but often miss.

In addition to counting steps this smart pedometer, when triggered, signals a cloud network to the status of any custom activity. This allows social groups and communities to join in and exercise together, whether walking the dog or going to school. Social groups can then grow further by selecting the shared activity and touching the devices together.

Information such as steps and calories are instantly uploaded online, providing social feedback and fitness monitoring as part of a healthy balanced lifestyle.

Ross Dudley
Industrial Design & Technology BA

Also on p.186

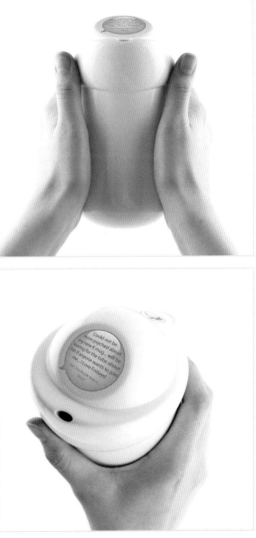

Human interaction is one of the fundamentals of wellbeing. As our society becomes more diverse, and the internet extends our communicative reach, we are drifting from interacting with those in our immediate community. But there is no reason that this same technology that lets us communicate instantaneously, with friends on the other side of the globe, cannot be used to create similar bonds with the people around us.

The challenge was to capture the essence of Kellogg's in this design for the consumer of 2025. The familiar characteristics of a ceramic coffee mug, inspired the design of an on-the-go hot drinks flask that uses the social networking status of people in your immediate proximity and community producing relevant notices to build conversation starters.

Social Together is for commuting adults who might go without a Kellogg's breakfast but will often have a hot drink on the way to work.

Michael Jones
Industrial Design & Technology BA

Also on p.192

Unwind Together
Future design concepts for Kellogg's

Unwind Together is a Kellogg's concept promoting sustained relationships.

When activated, the tray sends out an invitation to everyone in the K cloud network. This provides an incentive for others to pop around, say hello and unwind with a cup tea or coffee. Through wireless powered inductive technology, the tray also helps to prolong the experience by keeping the drink at the perfect temperature for longer. The sophisticated technology is shrouded by the simplicity of tray's form, adding to people's familiarity and perception. People feel at home with the technology.

After a long day at work it is nice to just sit back and relax and unwind. This period of the day is also a key social period between friends, families and communities. Linking many cultures, the tradition of a having a hot beverage is synonymous with relaxation and a friendly chat, allowing people to catch up, tell stories and unwind together.

Tobi Lawal
Mechanical Engineering & Design MEng

Also on p.194

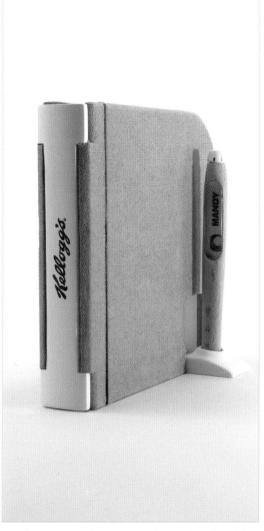

Keeping Together is a community enabler, breaking down generation barriers through inclusive design principles to bring advanced technology to a familiar, friendly and desirable product.

Using the recognisable form of a personal organiser and the practical function of a pen, the user is able to send and receive digital messages to anyone within their community. The product is aimed at older generations and will ensure social interaction with younger community members is possible, thus instigating and keeping social interaction between generations alive. Using the familiar and authentic method of putting pen to paper, all messages are converted into a digital format and sent by clicking the top of the pen; a very natural and unintimidating method of technological communication.

The product is also connected with the 'Kellogg's cloud' network and is capable of receiving updates from all other 'Kellogg's cloud' enabled products.

Also on p.201

Nick Harrod
Industrial Design & Technology BA

Growing Together
Future design concepts for Kellogg's

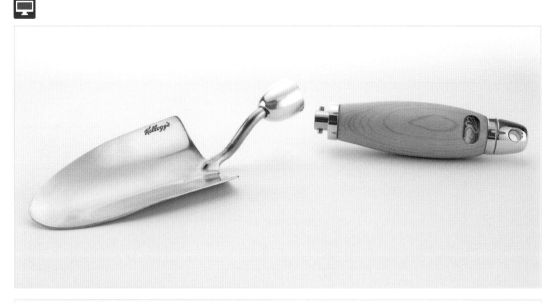

Growing Together is an interchangeable gardening tool that communicates the change in outdoor activity to the 'Kellogg's cloud network'.

The product aims to engage people with each other by making use of outdoor gardening space and local allotments. When connected and in use the tool updates the cloud to show that you are gardening, encouraging others to join in.

Different attachments indicate your gardening intent; whether it be seeding, cultivating or harvesting your crops. This allows novice gardeners to learn together as a community the pleasurable experience that growing your own produce can bring.

The produce can then be shared to encourage sustainable healthy living amongst the community.

Tom Etheridge
Industrial Design & Technology BA

Also on p.198

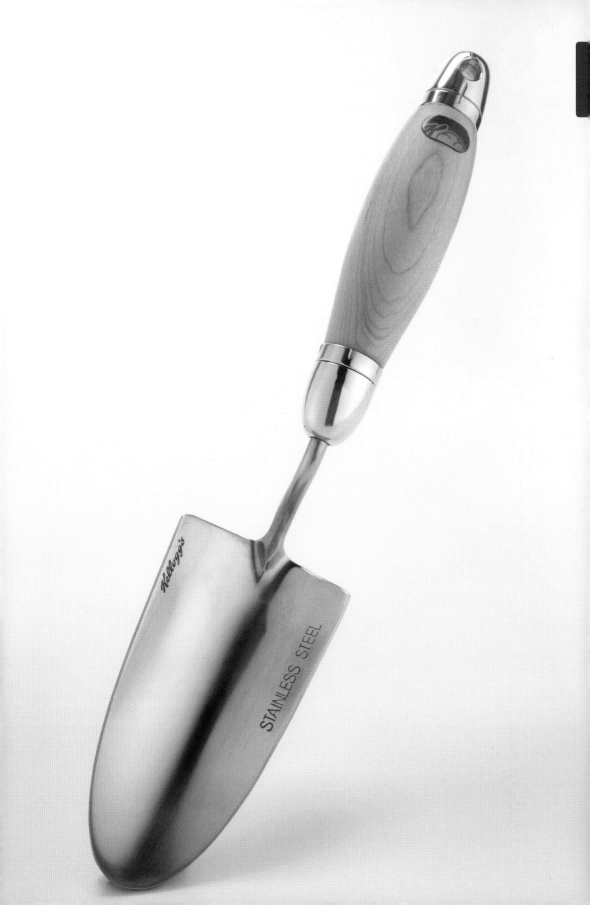

Play Pals
Future design concepts for müller

There is a growing trend for individuals to live alone in the UK, and this is on the rise. Coupled with a growing online community, the act of social interaction is changing, and will be very different by the year 2020. The müller brand is perfectly placed to look at this growing social trend by incorporating the cornerstones of the brand into the design of a product.

Play Pals encourage social interaction and networking between different friendship groups allowing müller's strong values to contribute to its success.

Allowing people to easily locate and communicate with their friends, Play Pals can set up various social activities such as games nights, sports events or cultural excursions. Using friendship groups and character sets allows the product to suggest inviting people from different groups who may have similar interests to the main group. An online müllerworld provides a platform to make best use of the growing internet trends to encourage and spark this social interaction. Character sets will allow the users to personalise their page.

Simon Smith
Industrial Design BSc

Also on p.209

With the changing family unit, more and more people live in multi-generational and extended families. Good communication is key to ensure the wellbeing of everyone within the family unit. Here müller have the potential to ensure good family relationships by enhancing current group activity.

Looking towards 2020, müller Tip Toes encourages activity by introducing a feedback system to measure achievement. A small on shoe monitor records the speed, distance and duration of the activity. When shoes are placed on the base unit it glows and sets targets according to their achievements. The more people in the group wearing the monitors, the better the feedback. This new level of feedback will encourage more of the family to get involved where a family walk might not have appealed to them before.

The group's progress can be tracked online in the 'müllerworld' environment with group achievements and targets given in more detail. Links can also be made with other families to encourage more activity.

Natalie King
Industrial Design BSc

Also on p.180

Family Friend
Future design concepts for müller

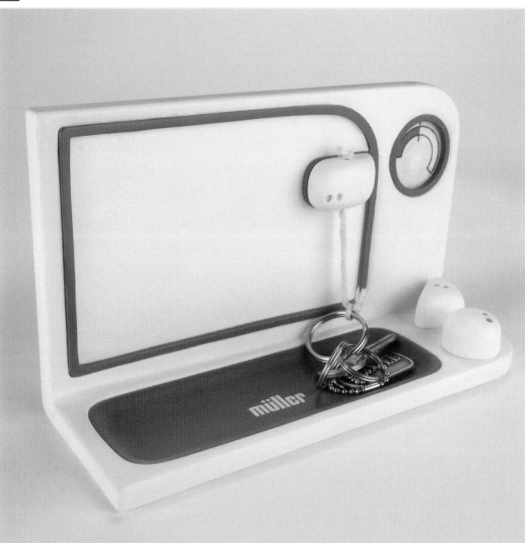

The family bond is key, and is what many people rely on during rough times in their life, but the family unit is in danger of falling apart, especially in our pressured lives. Currently people prefer to spend the little time they have by themselves rather than with their family, so something needs to be done.

The müller brand is prominent within the yoghurt industry, but it has the qualities, core values and ethics to potentially produce products that improve the family unit in 2020.

The müller Family Friend is a registery device in the form of a family key holder that will acknowledge when each family member returns home. This concept works via the use of müller character keychains that are attached to each member's keys. The characters are magnetic and connect to the key holder registering how many family members are home (müllerness level) and sending it to the 'müllerworld' website. This then allows each family to be able to track their time spent together. These keychains come in a range of characters, and allow individuality within the family.

Daniel Trigg
Industrial Design BSc

Also on p.86

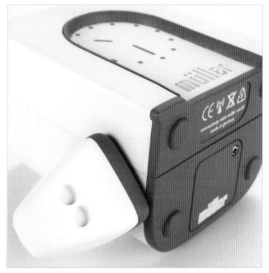

Taking on the rising cultural theme in which people interact less and less, Break Buddy attempts to prevent social meltdown. Whether it is a new gaming console, or through the booming internet industry, many products are denying face-to-face contact. Too often people get into a routine where they fail to appreciate the benefits of having like minded people around them. Break Buddy is aimed at the 9-5 working community, and takes advantage of this by trying to promote out of work activities.

The Break Buddy through the online 'müllerworld' enables and encourages colleagues to communicate and suggest activities for social interaction outside of the office. Whether going for a drink, a meal, or a session of sport, the Break Buddy alerts you of any invitation. By picking it up with a series of shakes you can respond to say whether you are able to attend. Allowing you to see your friend's status, 'müllerworld' offers a chance to see more specific details about social events. Available in a variety of forms the Break Buddy can be personalised between friends.

Luke Wilson
Industrial Design BSc

Also on p.68

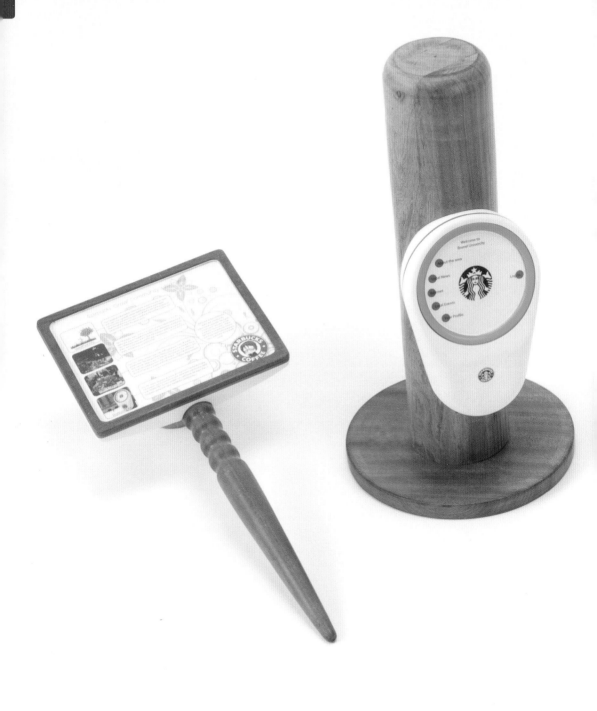

Intercom System
Future design concepts for Starbucks

Starbucks is ultimately about community. Intercom System provides people with an environment that they can feel safe in. Friendships and alliances are formed within Starbucks all around the world. This social concept projects that 'Starbucks feeling' of safety and security and turns it into products for the wider community.

The project is a public information system. The idea behind the system is to make information sharing public again, by taking it away from personal hand held devices and putting it back into public products that are shared by the community. It provides information such as local business listings, bus timetables, internet access etc. This way, if you find yourself in a new place, there will always be an easy way to access information about the area.

James Du Heaume
Industrial Design & Technology BA

Starbucks in 2025 will be at the forefront of community interaction. With people becoming divided in society, the Seedpod is a tool that allows for 'on-the-go' gardening and the cultivation of community friendship. In an age when technology has isolated people and separated us from nature, Starbucks is at the forefront of re-establishing and nurturing communication in society by enticing us out of our homes and back to nature. The product gives us another dimension when venturing outside, to plant seeds in ignored corners of our landscape, to tell others of our efforts and to monitor the growth of new plants, thereby fostering a sense of well-being.

The Seedpod allows its user to quickly plant a 'Seed bomb' in any area and relay their activity to fellow gardeners via the base when arriving home. New seedlings can then be checked and watered when needed. Seeing an area of previously neglected ground spring into life promotes wellbeing not just to the gardeners, but to the community at large who will grow together whilst watching their plants flourish.

Freddie Jordan
Industrial Design & Technology BA

Also on p.193

Coffee Mate
Future design concepts for Starbucks

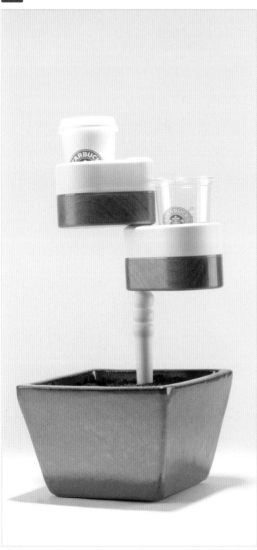

In 2025, our world will be a place even busier and more frantic than it is today. Community breakdown is a growing problem, as people no longer have the time or will to converse with their neighbours. The role of Starbucks has changed as they are now out in the community, helping to bring people together and get them talking. Communal areas such as allotments are excellent environments in which to undertake this task.

The Coffee Mate is a product that insulates Starbucks drinks, hot or cold keeping them safe from spillage. The stand is easy to set up and will hold a pair of beverages. As the stand holds two drinks, refreshment breaks can be held together, between fellow users of the allotment. This increases interaction and provides an enlightened sense of well being for both gardeners, while remaining close to Starbucks' core values and unique style.

Thomas Kelham
Industrial Design BSc

Also on p.30

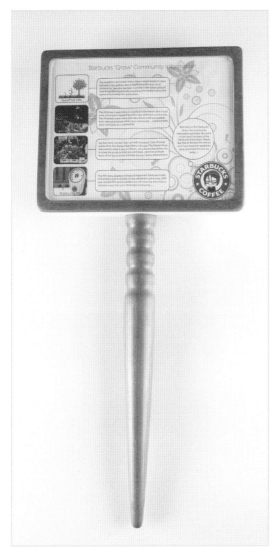

Starbucks Grow is an information-sharing device that enables communication within an allotment. The devices can be pulled from the ground and taken to the user's individual plot and allows them to communicate and share information with everyone else within the allotment.

With a simple interface the user will be able to select from viewing blogs, looking at other people's plots, sharing ideas, looking at local news and a market places. Once the user has finished at the allotment

they will simply return Starbucks Grow to any dedicated flowerbed. It encourages communication and nurture the well-being of all allotment communities in 2025.

Also on p.81

Rob Musselbrook
Industrial Design & Technology BA

the
network

A platform for knowledge transfer and exchange with our global partners

Made in Brunel is an international brand and has connected with partner institutions each year since its inception in 2006. In this innovative section you will find design and engineering from four world leading global partners.

Partners

Tsinghua University
Academy of Arts and Design, China

Tsinghua University, established in 1911, is one of China's foremost comprehensive research Universities. At present, the University has 13 schools and 55 departments with faculties in science, engineering, humanities, law, medicine, history, philosophy, economics, management, education and art. The University has now over 25,900 students, including 13,100 undergraduates and 12,800 graduate students. As one of China's most renowned Universities, Tsinghua has become an important institution for fostering talent and scientific research.

The educational philosophy of Tsinghua is to "train students with integrity". Among over 120,000 students who have graduated from Tsinghua, since its founding are many outstanding scholars, eminent entrepreneurs and great statesmen remembered and respected by their fellow Chinese citizens.

With the motto of "Self-Discipline and Social Commitment" and the attitude of "Actions Speak Louder than Words", Tsinghua University is dedicated to the well-being of Chinese society and to world development.

Indian Institute
of Technology Madras, India

Indian Institute of Technology Madras is one of the premier institutions of national importance in higher technical education and basic and applied research. It was established in 1959 by the Government of India in collaboration with assistance from the German Government.

The Institute has developed considerable academic infrastructure and earned an international reputation for excellence in education. The Institute has sixteen academic departments and a number of advanced research centres in various disciplines of engineering and pure sciences, with nearly 100 laboratories organised in a unique functioning pattern. It is a residential institution with almost 460 faculty members, approximately 4500 students and 1250 administrative supporting staff.

A faculty of international repute, a brilliant student community, excellent technical and supporting staff, as well as an effective administrative team have all contributed to the preeminent status of IIT Madras. The campus is located in the city of Chennai, previously known as Madras. Chennai is the state capital of Tamil Nadu, a southern state in India.

IIT Madras is committed to the advancement of knowledge through education and research, in both Pure and Applied Science, and within Engineering, Social Sciences and Humanities. The vision of IIT Madras is "To be an academic institution in dynamic equilibrium with its social, ecological and economic environment striving continually for excellence in education, research and technological service to the nation".

Rhode Island
School of Design, USA

Rhode Island School of Design is a global leader in educating creative people who aspire to make a meaningful contribution to our world.

Rhode Island School of Design (RISD) was founded in 1877 in Providence, Rhode Island and is a vibrant community of artists and designers that includes 2,200 students from around the world, approximately 350 faculty and curators, plus 400 staff members.In addition, each year more than 200 prominent artists, critics, authors and philosophers visit the historic College Hill campus.

The mission of the Rhode Island School of Design, through its college and museum, is to educate its students and the public in the creation and appreciation of works of art and design, to discover and transmit knowledge and to make lasting contributions to a global society through critical thinking, scholarship and innovation.

Simon Fraser University
Interactive Arts & Technology, USA

Named after an explorer, Simon Fraser, SFU opened in 1965. Taking only 30 months to grow from the idea stage into an almost completed campus with 2,500 students it was dubbed the "Instant University".

Just over 42 years later SFU has over 30,000 students and 100,000 alumni, more than 700 tenure-track faculty and 1,600 staff. The original campus has grown into three vibrant campuses in Burnaby, Vancouver and Surrey and SFU's reputation has grown into one of innovative teaching, research and community outreach.

Brunel University's School of Engineering and Design is particularly pleased to welcome Simon Fraser's renowned School of Interactive Arts and Technology to the Made in Brunel family in 2009.

Technologico De Monterrey, Mexico

The Tecnológico de Monterrey is a Mexican private educational institution that was founded in 1943. Currently its campus is distributed throughout the country, and academic centers in Mexico and other Latin American countries; it also has international offices in North America, Europe, and Asia. Through its Virtual University, students can study all over the world, by means of learning networks and advanced information technologies.

Our mission is to prepare upstanding, ethical individuals with a humanistic outlook, who are internationally competitive in their professional fields, and become committed to the economic, political, social, and cultural development of their communities and to the sustainable use of natural resources.

Through educational, and research and development programs, we prepare students and transfer knowledge:

- To promote businesses' international competitiveness based on knowledge, innovation, technological development, and sustainable development.

- To develop business management models capable of competing in a global economy.

- To create, implement and transfer business incubator models and networks in order to contribute to the creation of companies.

- To collaborate in professionalising public administration; and analyse and propose public policy for Mexico's development.

- To contribute to the community's sustainable development with innovative models and systems for its educational, social, economic and political advancement.

EasyClean

Helps with clothes caring in hotels

Although people always bring lots of clothes for change during a journey, it is still an inconvenience to clean underwear in a hotel.

EasyClean helps with clothes washing in a hotel. It contains a cleaning bag and a dryer. The cleaning bag is provided to each customer individually to make washing easier and compact. The surface mounted dryer provides efficient drying and caring for small clothes. The 15min process includes shake-drying, heat-drying and disinfecting by O3.

EasyClean provides a set of high quality services with current technology. It makes the journey much lighter for the customers; increase the high reputation of the hotel and creates a commercial opportunity for the service company.

Yu Fu

Tsinghua University

Urban Eyes
Providing a convenient solution for viewing city scenery

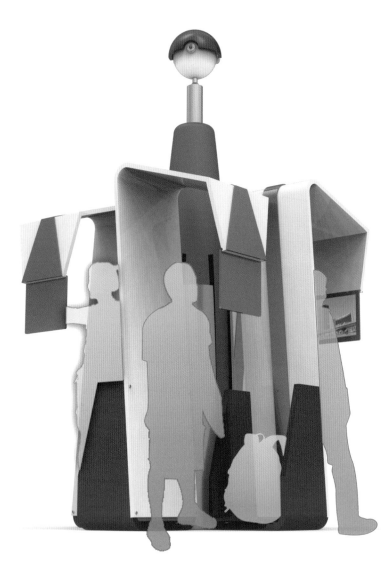

A common problem faced by tourists in cities is time management Due to the multitude of signs and activities available in urban areas, it can be difficult to decide where to go or what to do. In this situation, tourists can use Urban Eyes.

In famous locations and landmarks around the city numerous Urban Eyes would be installed. Each of them has a HD cam which shoots high quality videos and photos of the view surrounding it. Urban Eyes are connected in a network, so the travellers can enjoy seeing other real time sceneries of the city on the screen provided by the Urban Eyes. They can then decide which place to go next, or snap the video and download the photo to their cellphone making it memorable. This is the future of city experiences for tourists.

Xia Chenxi
Tsinghua University

Easy-Mover is a new stretcher design for evacuating the wounded in the emergency accidents and disasters such as earthquakes and hurricanes, specifically designed to reach places and ambulance cannot. It incorporates the principle of one-wheeled vehicles, used by Chinese people living in remote mountain villages. Easy-Mover is efficient and can be rapidly deployed. 1 or 2 adults can remove a wounded patient easily and transport them long distances.

The structural design of folding means Easy-Mover can change to suit the height of the patient, and it can be folded very compact for convenient transportation. In addition, it is easy to assemble, simple technological, low-cost and easy to recycle.

Luo Jianping
Tsinghua University

Partly Cloudy

Providing an efficient solution for post-earthquake emergency

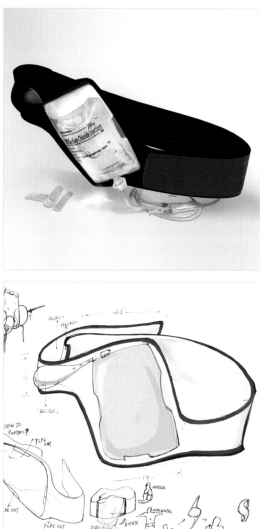

After an earthquake, victims can suffer from muscle necrosis, if they have been trapped under rubble and debris for more than 24 hours. Once they have been rescued, large amounts of toxins released from necroses will cause sudden death from Acute Kidney Injure (AKI). Thus, victims need to be given physiological saline before release to ensure effective metabolism.

Partly Cloudy is designed for emergent transfusion in earthquake and other emergency scenarios. The medicine bag is squeezed by the air pressure around it, so liquid can drip out of the bag without being hung-up. Free from the dependence on gravity, without use of stents and other devices, the medicine bag can be laid on or wrapped anywhere.

Partly Cloudy is efficient, easy to use and suitable for various of situations. Since alcohol swabs, band-aids, sterile infusion sets and other appliances are packed together, it will become a consecutive workflow of sterilising, inflation and transfusion. Partly Cloudy has a long belt with Velcro, making it easy to be fastened conveniently to the arm, waist or a stretcher.

Qianjun Wu

Tsinghua University

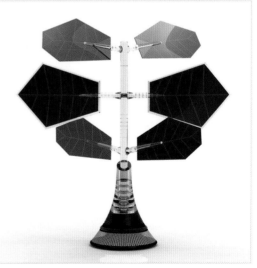

Respiration and photosynthesis are two main physical processes of plants. One converts energy while the other exchanges air. This unique property of plants formed the basis for a revolutionary solar powered air purifier.

This product is designed for low-carbon lifestyle in daily life. Users place the Man-Made Plant in the sun to charge, and then use it to purify the air. To maximise the absorption of sunlight inclination of the sun, every segment of the caudex is rotatable. Like a plant, all of the leaves rotate to face the light as the sun moves. The leaves are all designed like those of a tree to receive maximum sun light.

Chen Xingnuo
Tsinghua University

Haunted World

Merging fantasy and reality through multiplayer location-based gaming

The technology powering videogame consoles has allowed developers to create extremely immersive and challenging games. Unfortunately, this level of engagement comes at a cost. Gamers have become disconnected with the environment and all the people surrounding them.

The goal of Haunted World is to reconnect gamers to the physical world. By using the technology found on SmartPhones and a backend powered by a robust web engine, we created an augmented reality game that will encourage players to explore and experience the actual environment while engaged in an immersive multiplayer gaming experience.

Project Team:

Bruce McLavy
Frankie Yan
Lok To Chau
M. Yigit Karakilic
Paul Yuan

Simon Fraser University, Canada

Braillet
Social-aided communication for visually impaired people

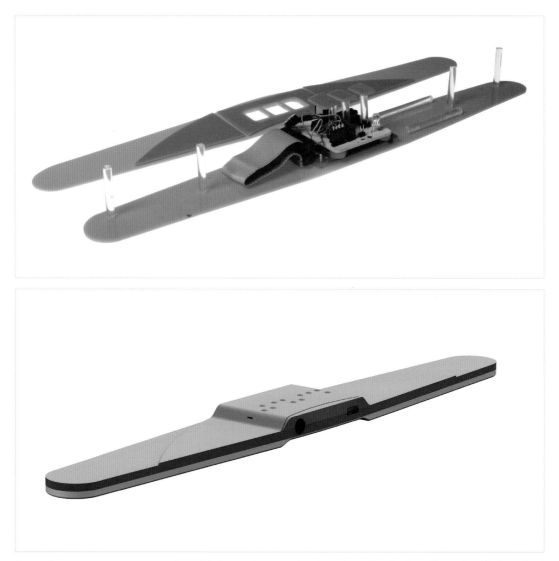

Every day, an enormous quantity of information is transmitted in hundreds of languages, across thousands of different channels and media, making communications an essential social tool. A large percentage of the population however, have issues with traditional forms of communication, modern social media tools are not wholly inclusive of visually impaired individuals, rendering them isolated from their contemporaries. The Braillet is a system founded in Social Intelligence Design, which provides unobtrusive access to social channels using bracelets. The devices allow visually impaired users to interact with social media and networks in an intuitive manner. Additionally, users may use the device to capture and treasure memories sonically in phonographs. The Braillet is an innovate solution to generating inclusive social networks by allowing visually impaired and fully sighted people to communicate fully.

César Alegría Flores, Diana Amaya Rosas, Albany Gómez Limón, César Alberto Quintero Ugalde, Diego Rafael Torres Lafuente

Technologico De Monterrey, Mexico

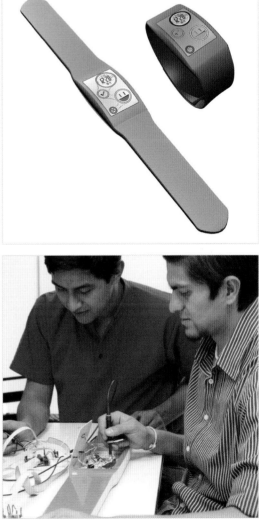

IUPY is a unique entertainment system based on the principles of Social Intelligence Design, focused on proving that gaming is not just about the game itself but about social interactions and conviviality. IUPY was designed to dissolve the bubble of alienation which common gaming platforms establish. IUPY bracelets allow gamers to engage with each other socially, something which PDAs and smart phones cannot do in the context of portable online gaming. The bracelets and base stations work together to allow users to manage games and gaming requests within their own microcosms. Once a game has started, players may remove their bracelets transforming them into controllers. IUPY bracelets keep gaming spontaneous, and accessible whilst removing the need to carry around additional equipment and pocket clutter.

Samuel Isaac Delgado Durón, José Antonio García Nieves. Sergio Paul González Isidoro, César Paul Neria Hernández, Begoña Rodríguez Mondragón

Technologico De Monterrey, Mexico

Cat-Mandü

The storyteller friend for children

Cat-Mandü is a story-telling companion for children who are away from home; bonds between parents and their children are maintained by a friendly plush toy. Cat-Mandü was developed using Social Intelligence Design techniques to improve the emotional aspects of the product through meaningful interaction. Parents can record their voices directly into Cat-Mandü for later playback, enabling them to continue the time-honoured tradition of reading stories to their children with all the emotion and feeling of the spoken word, even from afar.

Parents may also send hugs to their children via Cat-Mandü using SMS. The plushie is manufactured from child friendly fabrics, which are soft and warm encouraging unabashed physical interaction in order to relay the closeness and warmth of home.

Andrea Chávez Solís, Ana Varenka De la Vega Díaz, Norma Alejandra Enzástiga Ulloa, Luis Daniel Manríquez Pedraza, José Antonio Martínez Rivera

Technologico De Monterrey, Mexico

The growing global waste crisis fuels the current search for alternative high-impact methods to sustainably manage refuse.

Green Code is a new recycling system that aims to motivate users to recycle and dispose of their waste responsibly by offering an economical incentive.

The project was developed to alter user perception and behaviour through social awareness, which should ultimately lead to social attitude changes and reforms.

Damariz Gárate Flores, Francisco Javier López Casique, Servando José López Morales, Israel Salas Velasco, Carmen Georgina Walther Silesky

Technologico De Monterrey, Mexico

BGR
Intelligent awareness table

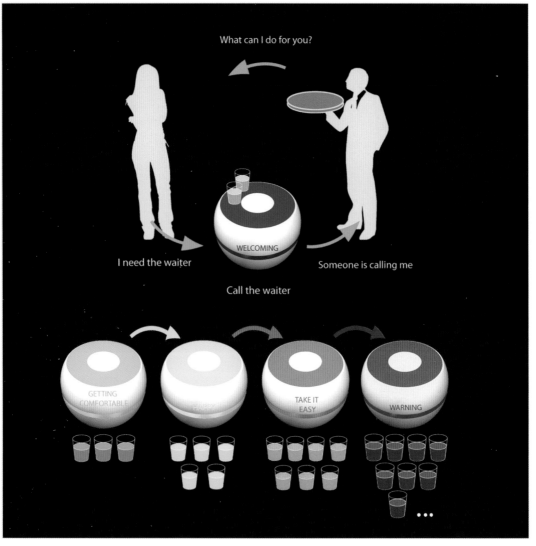

In Mexico, the legal blood alcohol content limit for driving is 0.08%; individuals caught with higher levels of blood alcohol face serious penalization. The BGR intelligent table provides a fluid and efficient method for informing patrons and waiters about their current consumption levels. Utilising the psychology of colour to generate implicit social awareness, the table lighting changes trough five colour phases to indicate how much the guests at a particular table have consumed. Those wishing to drive home should stop drinking, as the table turns yellow. Patrons sitting at orange or red tables should not be allowed to drive and through social association those around them will be subtly aware of this. Additionally the coloured tables warn those sitting at them once they are past the limit.

Angel Allende Tomas, Karla Hernández Siu, Luis Jakousi Martínez Ambrosio, Irvin Alan Ocampo Franco, Gabriel Salvador Tejeda

Technologico De Monterrey, Mexico

People can be unaware of how their behaviour negatively affects the environment and endangers the natural world. Building the foundations of energy consumption awareness must be tackled early on to make any lasting change on behavioural patterns. The Bots develop childrens' social skills as well as introducing an awareness of water and power usage. Using bracelets and a centralised base station the products help children keep track of their consumption statistics at home. The Bots transform energy saving into a game, promoting friendly competition in social groups. Rotating teams must learn to work together to do better than their peers. The intuitive bracelets allows the data required for measured sustainable behaviour to seamlessly permeate through the collective consciousness of a social group.

Estefania Larracoechea González, Gonzalo Pacheco Bravo, Jorge Eduardo Raigosa Guevara, Alejandro Martin Berger Saunders

Technologico De Monterrey, Mexico

Page Flipper
Flips pages on demand

Tech-Met
A safety helmet capable of sending SOS alerts

Page Flipper aims to assist people with restricted hand mobility in flipping pages while reading. It is also helpful for musicians who find it difficult to turn pages while performing. Another major use of this product would be for digitising books.

The device is actuated using two buttons, one for each direction. Vacuum suction is used to lift the page, two L-shaped links are used to flip and clamp it in place. The links have been optimized for time to perform the actions of supporting, flipping and clamping.

Team:
Bhavin Gawali
Hem Rampal

According to a survey carried out by NHTSA, the highest number of motorbike accidents occur in off road areas and during night rides.

Tech-Met helps in providing prompt support services like ambulance and police by sending the details about the approximate location of accidents.

Whenever an accident takes place, a sudden high velocity force is experienced by the rider. Tech-met has an in-built accelerometer which measures the intensity of this force and in case it is beyond a certain threshold, the cell-phone is triggered using Bluetooth interface through a microcontroller. The cell phone then sends an SMS or a pre-recorded call to the national police and ambulance services, providing them with the exact location of the accident using GPS technology and thereby resulting in timely action by the support facilities.

By Mohit Mittal

Indian Institute of Technology Madras

Smart Streets
An automatic street lighting system to save power

Street lights are switched on in the evening and remain on throughout the night even in the absence of any vehicles on the roads. Traffic density drops to less than half of its normal value between 1am and 5am in the night. Smart Streets is expected to save about one-third of the power consumption during these times.

Smart Streets uses sensors that detect a vehicle, and switches on a specific set of street lights. A vehicle on Smart Street is guaranteed to have 200m of visibility at any point of time. Events such as multiple cars on the road, and some vehicle stopping unexpectedly on the road are addressed with this energy saving system for future urban lanscapes.

Team:
Neerav Karani
Srinath Sibi

Indian Institute of Technology Madras

343

Brunel: Past, Present and Future

Isambard Kingdom Brunel (1806-1859)

In the century leading up to 1860, the Industrial Revolution caused a period of economic and social upheaval in Britain, driven by a small group of engineers. Isambard Kingdom Brunel was perhaps the most exceptional of this group, and many of his challenging and inspiring works, have survived to our own time.

Entering his father's business at the age of 20, Brunel's first project was to drive a tunnel under the Thames from Rotherhithe to Wapping – a complex feat of engineering. At 26, he was appointed engineer to the newly-formed Great Western Railway; his civil engineering works on the line between London and Bristol are still used by today's high-speed trains, demonstrating the quality and endurance of his designs. The project encompassed not just the rails, but also viaducts and stations.

His other works included the Clifton Suspension Bridge over the River Avon, which was finished after Brunel's death in 1864, as well as a remarkable prefabricated hospital, complete with air-conditioning and drainage system, for use in the Crimean War. He worked on three major ship-building projects: the Great Western, Great Britain and Great Eastern. They were launched between 1837 and 1859 representing leaps forward in naval architecture.

As his sketchbooks and notebooks show, Brunel concerned himself with every aspect of his projects, from the grace of a design to the precision of its execution. His great achievement was to marry his engineering vision with supporting calculation and experimentation. He faced inevitable setbacks and disappointments, sometimes suffering personal financial loss through bankrolling his ventures. He readily admitted his mistakes but never let them daunt him.

Brunel died of a stroke on 15 September 1859. Despite his short career, he is remembered as one of the most illustrious engineers of his time, and his achievements still inspire designers and engineers the world over. His example is a particular inspiration to the staff and students of the university named in his honour.

The history and ethos of Brunel University

Brunel is a world-class university based in Uxbridge, West London. Our distinctive approach combines academic rigour with the practical, entrepreneurial and imaginative approach pioneered by our namesake, Isambard Kingdom Brunel.

The University was founded in 1966 as a new kind of institution dedicated to providing research and teaching that could be applied to the needs of industry and society. This goal was central in the creation of our Royal Charter, one of the most progressive and visionary charters of its day. It emphasises the University's commitment to ensuring academic learning, is relevant and that teaching and research benefit both individuals and society at large.

The confidence and sense of purpose that characterise today's Brunel stem from this principle, which is still essential to our Mission; "to advance knowledge and understanding and provide society with confident, talented and versatile graduates" and our vision; "to be a world-class creative community that is inspired to work, think and learn together to meet the challenges of the future".

Research is at the heart of all we do. We place great value on the usefulness of our research, which improves our understanding of the world around us and informs up-to-the-minute teaching as well as creating opportunities for collaborative work with business, industry and the public sector. Brunel's research ethos generates an atmosphere of innovation which inspires students and staff throughout the University, as well as encouraging the sharing of ideas and expertise for which we are renowned for.

Brunel's reputation is built on its groundbreaking work in subjects as diverse as design, engineering, education, science, sociology, IT, psychology, law and business. That reputation has gradually spread to new areas, including the performing arts, journalism, environmental science and sport and health; research and teaching in these areas still retains the same outward-looking philosophy.

A long succession of developments and mergers, particularly those which transformed Acton Technical College into Brunel University and which later saw Brunel merge with Shoreditch College and the West London Institute, have brought the University from modest beginnings to become a major force both within the UK higher education sector and on the international stage.

Building a new Brunel

Brunel's campus has been transformed over the last few years. The University's investment in buildings and infrastructure is now approaching £300 million, with many new and refurbished social, teaching and sporting facilities, and more green spaces around campus.

We now boast world-class sports facilities, a renovated Lecture Centre and Students' Union. The library features a hugely increased book and journal collection, more computer workstations, more group study areas and an Assistive Technology Centre for disabled students. We have brought our campus accommodation up to 4,549 rooms in 34 halls of residence with our new Isambard Complex.

A new residential development, the Isambard Complex, has brought our campus accommodation up to 4,549 rooms in 34 halls of residence.

The Schools of Health Science & Social Care and Engineering & Design have benefited from new buildings and facilities. A £30 million flagship building at the main entrance to the University is scheduled for completion in 2012, providing a new home for the Brunel Business School as well as an auditorium and art gallery.

Since the 1960s, Brunel University has provided high quality academic programmes which meet the needs of the real world and contribute in a practical way to progress in all walks of life. We are very proud of the University's development and of its contributions to the empowerment of individuals and to the progress of society.

Brunel: School of Engineering and Design

School of Engineering and Design

Through the innovative engineering achievements of Isambard Kingdom Brunel, Brunel University's School of Engineering and Design is directly linked to recognition of the transformative power of innovation through design and engineering. With over 2500 undergraduate, postgraduate and research students the School is one of the largest and most successful in the UK and is renowned for its teaching, research and most importantly for the achievements of its graduates.

Innovation that works, the by-line for the work represented in this book, signifies the practical, industrial and social relevance of the School's work. This is an important distinguishing feature. On the undergraduate courses a high percentage of students complete a year working in industry, enhancing their practical skills and career opportunities. Much of the research and project work within the School has links with industrial partners across an incredible variety of sectors.

This breadth is also reflected in the expertise within the School which is organised within five broad subject areas:

- Advanced Manufacturing and Enterprise Engineering
- Civil Engineering
- Design
- Electronic & Computer Engineering
- Mechanical Engineering

Underpinning all of our work is a an incredible level of energy, ambition and belief that our subjects and expertise can make a positive contribution to a rapidly evolving world and the challenges we face.

Just as IK Brunel's work was at the heart of the industrial revolution, Brunel University's School of Engineering and Design is at the heart of innovating for the 21st Century.

Design

Undergraduate Design courses:
- Industrial Design and Technology BA
- Product Design BSc
- Product Design Engineering BSc

Postgraduate Design:
- 3 specialist MA and MSc courses

Admissions Tutor:
Stephen Green
stephen.green@brunel.ac.uk

Electronic and Computer Engineering

Undergraduate Electronic and Computer Engineering:
- Broadcast Media (Design and Technology) BSc
- Communication Networks Engineering BEng/MEng
- Computer Systems Engineering BEng/MEng
- Electronic and Electrical Engineering (Communication Systems) BSc/MEng
- Electronic and Electrical Engineering BEng/MEng
- Electronic and Microelectronic Engineering BEng
- Internet Engineering BEng
- Mobile Computing BSc
- Multimedia Technology and Design BSc

Postgraduate Electronic and Computer Engineering:
- 5 specialist MSc courses

Admissions Tutor:
Professor John Stapleton
john.stapleton@brunel.ac.uk

Design and Engineering Courses

Mechanical Engineering

Undergraduate Mechanical Engineering:
- Aerospace Engineering BEn/ MEng
- Aviation Engineering BEng/MEng
- Aviation Engineering with Pilot Studies BEng/MEng
- Mechanical Engineering BEng/MEng
- Mechanical Engineering with Aeronautics BEng/MEng
- Mechanical Engineering with Automotive Design BEng/MEng
- Mechanical Engineering with Building Services BEng/MEng
- Motorsport Engineering BEng/MEng

Postgraduate Mechanical Engineering:
- 8 specialist MSc courses

Admissions Tutor:
Petra Gratton
petra.gratton@brunel.ac.uk

Advanced Manufacturing and Enterprise Engineering (AMEE)

4 Specialist MSc courses

Enquires:
sed-pg-admissions@brunel.ac.uk

Civil Engineering

Undergraduate Civil Engineering courses:
- Civil Engineering with Sustainability BEng/MEng

Course Director:
Dr Philip Collins
ce.ug.admission@brunel.ac.uk

West London Innovation

The quadrant of London sweeping out from Kensington and Chelsea, encompassing Wembley Stadium, Heathrow Airport and the Thames, M4 and M40 corridor travelling westwards is one of the most economically successful and vibrant regions in the world. West London comprises of more than 750,000 jobs and 67,000 businesses, which annually contribute over £27 billion to the UK economy. Heathrow, the worlds most successful airport, is a natural global hub for the world. The region has a tremendous track record as a home for innovative business at the cutting edge of global markets including the likes of GSK, BA, Disney, Diagio and BSkyB. Joint research conducted in 2007/8 amongst large corporates and SME's in West London and funded by the London Development Agency, clearly showed the high level of innovation achievement within West London whilst also identifying a keen appetite for sharing and gaining more knowledge on emerging innovation methods and techniques.

Collaborations between business and universities are increasingly recognised as important catalysts for innovation and economic regeneration. Many of the people and projects which make up MADE IN BRUNEL exemplify collaborations to harness the energy, creativity, research and knowledge available within the entrepreneurial spirit of the area. The following organisations and initiatives are part of the infrastructure within West London to provide practical support to facilitate connections and the innovation which can flow from these:

West London Partnership

Chief executives and leaders of the six local authorities in West London and senior staff both from large corporate businesses and from SMEs based in West London join forces as WLP to develop the overall social and economic interests of the region. This dynamic partnership between business and local authorities has a broad remit including transport, regeneration, skills and workforce development, spatial development, planning and property, and housing.

West London Business

Whatever your size and whatever your sector, West London Business can help your business grow and compete. With a series of top quality business information and networking events, a strong lobbying and representation profile and a membership brimming with businesses from across the sub-region, West London Business is the premier business network.
www.westlondon.com

Designplus

Designplus represents design interests and facilitates events, training and collaborative projects in all aspects of design. Particularly within important emerging areas such as sustainable design, design for health and human centered design.
www.designplus.org.uk

West London Innovation

Is a joint initiative led by Brunel University and West London Business which seeks to inspire, inform, share and promote innovation within businesses, not for profit groups, public bodies, academic organisations and individuals in West London.
www.westlondoninnovation.net

Acknowledgements

The creation of this book has been an extraordinary effort by so many busy people who have given their time to make this possible. We would like to thank the whole of the Made in Brunel team, the staff from the Brunel University School of Engineering and Design, our sponsers, business partners and the many individuals and companies across the world who have created this innovative publication.

Many thanks to you all.

index
and contacts

Student Index

Peter Abel
Industrial Design & Technology BA

e: Peter@peterabel.co.uk
w: www.peterabel.co.uk
t: 07847530115

 71

Bola Adetujoye
Industrial Design & Technology BA

e: bola889@msn.com
w: www. bolasdesigns.co.uk
t: 07958425922

Hard working, enthusiastic and full of passion! Enjoys designing creative solutions that will help improve people's lives.

 025 Q 52

Ahmed Shuaib
Industrial Design BSc

e: shuaibahmed60@hotmail.com
t: 07809156794

I have always had a keen eye for innovation and design. I find the challenge design presents motivating and this is exactly what I want to be doing on a daily basis.

 53

Jonathan Aihun
Industrial Design & Technology BA

e: johnathanaihun@hotmail.co.uk
t: 07850183390

I take great interest in all aspects of design and its process. I study jazz music and its electronic variations in my spare time.

 27 👥 238

Irvin Alan Ocampo Franco
Tecnológico de Monterrey, Campus Querétaro

e: hyper_irvin@hotmail.com
w: www.qro.itesm.mx
t: +52 (442) 1795737

Think simple, make conscious. It only takes one light and one colour to make a change.

 340

César Alberto Quintero Ugalde
Tecnológico de Monterrey, Campus Querétaro

e: alberto.ugalde13@gmail.com
w: www.qro.itesm.mx
t: 52 (448) 2780398

Technology should always help never hinder.

 336

César Alegría Flores
Tecnológico de Monterrey, Campus Querétaro

e: nio55_3@hotmail.com
w: www.qro.itesm.mx
t: +52 (448) 1022725

The technology needs to be used as a benefit for the future generations.

 336

Norma Alejandra Enzástiga Ulloa
Tecnológico de Monterrey

e: ale.enzastiga@gmail.com
w: www.qro.itesm.mx
t: +52 (442) 1561657

Crazyness doesn´t border on the line of creativity. It is creativity.

 338

Angel Allende Tomas
Tecnológico de Monterrey, Campus Querétaro

e: aat_x@hotmail.com
w: www.qro.itesm.mx
t: +52 (442) 2383359

Realistic. Face challenges. Effort on everything.

 340

Fenella Allery
Aviation Engineering MEng

e: fenellaallery@gmail.com

My engineering strengths are Aerodynamics and Computational Fluid Dynamics. I am also a Flight Commander in the RAF Reserves, responsible for 30 Officer Cadets.

 175

Rita Almeida
Design and Branding Strategy MA

e: ritara33@hotmail.com
t: 07928701543

A creative Design and Branding Strategist who truly believes Design can facilitate users' lives. My focus in on User centred Design, Emotional Branding, Wellness and Beauty.

 271

José Antonio Martínez Rivera
Tecnológico de Monterrey, Campus Querétaro

e: hidrogallo@hotmail.com
w: www.qro.itesm.mx
t: +52 (442) 2847373

Knowledge is based on everyday learning and the opportunities presented on our daily life.

 338

Jorge Alvarez Picasso
Integrated Product Design MSc

e: jalvapic@gmail.com
t: 07910758547

I am a balanced designer with a constant desire to learn. Confidently mixing passion, creativity and precision into everything I produce.

 279

Richard Archer
Integrated Product Design MSc

e: contact@radesign.eu
w: www.radesign.eu
t: 07814747577

I believe that designers have the ability to promote positive change within society and it is this responsibility that drives my design process.

 276

Diana Amaya Rosas
Tecnológico de Monterrey, Campus Querétaro

e: Di.Diana.Amaya@gmail.com
w: www.qro.itesm.mx
t: +52 (442) 23645692

Design is the mobile of my soul, my heart is my muse; together they make the perfect combination to keep me creating beautiful things.

 336

Mark Ayres
Integrated Product Design MSc

e: mark.ayres@btinternet.com
t: 07734867743

Product Design graduate, MSc focus on Design Research to facilitate simple and effective design in order to sustain and improve our lifestyles further.

 277

Russell Anley
Industrial Design & Technology BA

e: ranley@gmail.com
t: 07507862948

Love foreign travel and having a knock about at squash. Aiming for a career in consumer medical product design and enjoying the rewards of making a difference.

 90   151

Andrew Bailey
Product Design BSc

e: akbmustang@hotmail.com
t: 07775603696

An avid golfer; aviation enthusiast and collector of model aeroplanes who prefers a good sketch or drawing over CAD. Well travelled and appreciative of other cultures and ways of life.

232

José Antonio García Nieves
Tecnológico de Monterrey, Campus Querétaro

e: ga_na87@hotmail.com
w: www.qro.itesm.mx
t: +52 (442) 3210428

In my project I applied all my knowledge about electronics while developing my potential as a future engineer.

 337

David Baker
Product Design BSc

e: david_baker87@hotmail.com
w: www.davidbakerdesigns.co.uk
t: 07910206722

 91

357

Network Directory
Ba - Ch

Travis Baldwin
Design and Branding Strategy MA

e: TravisBaldwin@hotmail.com
w: www.coroflot.com/travis_baldwin
t: 07897538707

My strengths combine product and strategic design tools to understand brands, create focused solutions, and lead teams.

 261

Adrian Bliss
Industrial Design & Technology BA

e: adrianbliss@sky.com
w:
t: 07807459844

Understanding the person for whom a product is designed, is what I believe facilitates good design. Good design is also unobtrusive, honest, long lasting, and consequent to the last detail.

 157  182

Daniel Bancroft
Aerospace Engineering MEng

e: sales@pr-zone.co.uk
t: 07985482166

175

Andrew Bonjour
Motorsport Engineering MEng

t: 07837613880

168

James Bartlett
Industrial Design BSc

e: james.bartlett@jmeb.co.uk
w: www.jmeb.co.uk
t: 07958463270

100

Max Borgeat
Product Design BSc

e: Max_borgeat@hotmail.co.uk
w: www.maxborgeat.com
t: 07775613424

"Beautiful Evidence is about the theory and practice of analytical design" Edward Tufte.

181

Daniel Beavis
Product Design BSc

e: Daniel.beavis@hotmail.com
w: www.danielbeavis.co.uk
t: 07825669797

Both creative and technical, enjoys developing functional aspects of concepts. Quick to learn, keen to develop professionally and personally. Siemens Placement.

72 106

Ben Boutcher-West
Industrial Design & Technology BA

e: ben.boutcher-west@live.com
t: 07944989996

I am an outgoing, motivated individual with good people skills and strong drive to achieve. I love adventure thriving on experience and enhancing it for others.

148 183

Hena Bhatti
Multimedia Technology & Design BSc

e: Hena_hikarusama@hotmail.com
t: 07810245643

287

Richard Braine
Product Design BSc

e: Richard.Braine@googlemail.com
w: www.Richard-Braine.com
t: 07502311780

Brunel has helped develop my understanding and thirst for design. The engineering side of the course has allowed me to become more than a 'felt-tip fairy'.

 107 215

Nathan Brown
Industrial Design & Technology BA

e: nathan_f_brown@hotmail.com
t: 07515414133

Emotive, creative and innovative designer.
Thinks outside the box. Occasionally lives
outside the box.

 73   154

Isambard Kingdom Brunel
Innovator

e: info@madeinbrunel.com
w: www.madeinbrunel.com
t: 01895 267776

My passion is to change the world, to harness
the power of steam and iron and push man to
limits they have never before seen.

 208

Tanya Budd
Product Design Engineering BSc

e: tanya@hypohoist.co.uk
w: www.hypohoist.co.uk
t: 07905279969

Through design and engineering it is possible
to help shape our future, which to me is an
exciting challenge.

 102

Richard Burgess
Mechanical Engineering BEng

e: richardgrahamburgess@live.com
w: joepedro.com
t: 07773784036

 105

Emily Calladine
Integrated Product Design MSc

e: mail@emilycalladine.com
w: www.emilycalladine.com
t: 0 7921817272

Passionate and creative, with an enthusiasm
for people centred solutions that drive
business.

 278

Chau Lok To
Simon Fraser University

e: readinisbad4health@hotmail.com
t: 1-604-771-3030

Art allows us to transcend our physical
constraints releasing our full potential as
creative beings. I strive to use design as a tool
for good.

 334

Andrea Chávez Solís
Tecnológico de Monterrey, Campus Querétaro

e: info@madeinbrunel.com
w: www.madeinbrunel.com
t: 01895 267776

My passion is to change the world, to harness
the power of steam and iron and push man to
limits they have never before seen.

 338

Xia Chenxi
Tsinghua University

e: aniltoora@hotmail.com
w: www.aniltoora.com
t: 86-10-62798872

Live and work with all your heart.

 330

Yannick Cheung
Motorsport Engineering MEng

t: 07928693885

 168

David Christensen
Multimedia Technology & Design BSc

e: kiwidaja@yahoo.com
t: 07599425026

I am and 2D/3D animator and concept artist
with a diverse skill set. I excel at creating
intellectual properties that are cathartic,
taking hold of the imagination and refusing
to let go.

295

Christy Chung
Design and Branding Strategy MA

e: christy.chung@live.com
t: 02089984621

Aspiring brand strategist, Passion for contemporary art, inspired by eco-design. "The best ideas come as jokes. Make your thinking as funny as possible." - Ogilvy.

 260

Luis Daniel Manríquez Pedraza
Tecnológico de Monterrey, Campus Querétaro

e: luisdaniel.manriquezpedraza@gmail.com
w: . www.qro.itesm.mx
t: +52 (442) 1970553

Nothing can function without the two main elements. Planning and organization.

 338

Charles Cooke
Industrial Design & Technology BA

e: charliecook21@googlemail.com
t: 07846269549

I have developed a solid understanding of envrional issues and hope to develop passive and eco housing solutions.

 29 131

Christina Daniels
Design and Branding Strategy MA

e: cppconsultants@live.com
w: www.creativepiedpiper.carbonmade.com/
t: 07828934992

Freelance graphic and apparel designer, and founder of thecoolcrewblog.com.

 259

Ben Curnow
Industrial Design & Technology BA

e: ben@bencurnow.co.uk
w: www.bencurnow.co.uk
t: 07793742686

All-round designer who enjoys many aspects of design, with a special passion for, 2D and 3D graphics.

 285

Ben Davey
Industrial Design BSc

e: bendavey@gmail.com
w: www.bendavey.co.uk
t: 07999714370

My strengths are strong communication and 3D design. I love drawing, Catia, workshop, bikes, beer and photography; just not at the same time.

 92 222

Anne Dah
Industrial Design & Technology BA

e: annemarie.dah@gmx.ch
w:
t: 07783511066

The more creative I get the happier I am

54

Loïc De Buck
Integrated Product Design MSc

e: loic@debuck.co.uk
w: www.debuck.co.uk
t: 07510206247

Passionate product developer with an interest in renewable energy.-Bachelor in Product Development (Antwerp)-Winner of the Student Lighting Design Awards 2008.

 40

Yvonne Dalton
Product Design Engineering BSc

e: Yvonne@epencil.co.uk
w: www.epencil.co.uk
t: 07891686972

This course follows steep learning curves, contains admiration for arty things and picks holes in functional failures.

 184

Matt Debnam
Product Design Engineering BSc

e: matthewdebnam@hotmail.co.uk
t: 07599711903

The success of a design should be measured by the change it causes in somebody's life rather than the complexity of its function. I want to change how we live.

 284

Hiral Desai
Integrated Product Design BSc

e: hirald87@gmail.com
t: 07709595090

"Limitations live only in our minds"
- Jamie Paolinetti.

 277

Ross Dudley
Industrial Design & Technology BA

e: dudders@blackberry.orange.co.uk
t: 07970740638

Design is about producing verbs aswell as
nouns. Observing a person's behaviour as well
as the problem to produce a solution through a
human-centred approach.

 186  306

Oliver Diebel
Product Design Engineering BSc

e: diebes_854@msn.com
t: 07891261006

An enthusiastic Product Design Engineer with
experience of CAD and design for manufacture
in the automotive industry

 93

Desiree Dundar
Design and Branding Strategy MA

e: asena_d@hotmail.com
t: 07964912528

Not a designer, but a dreamer...

 262

Simon Dingle
Motorsport Engineering MEng

e: simon_dingle@hotmail.com
t: 07886349525

Of making many books there is no end and much
study wearies the body ... therefore fear God and
obey all His commandments, for this is the entire
duty of man. (Ecclesiastes 12v12-13)

 168

Richard Dune
Mechanical Engineering BEng

e: richdunes@gmail.com
w:
t: 07888641249

I am a highly committed individual who is
analytical, honest, and reliable; motivated
and takes pride in a job well done.

 105

Rebecca Doggett
Industrial Design & Technology BA

e: beckydoggett@hotmail.com
w: joepedro.com
t: 07912755511

Imaginative and reflective with a flair for
graphic design and an interest in sustainable
and social design.

 26 134

Jorge Eduardo Raigosa Guevara
Course

e: jorgeraigosa@gmail.com
w:
t: +52(442) 1862190

Electronics engineering guys think in binary,
but in their hearts thinks just for help

 341

James Du Heaume
Industrial Design & Technology BA

e: Jayduheaume@hotmail.com
w: www. Jamesduheaumedesign.co.uk
t: 07972181767

My interests mainly lie in graphics and CAD
modelling, but I am actively interested in all
areas of product design. Check out my website
for more details.

 320

Shaun Eldred
Industrial Design & Technology BA

e: eldred_shaun@hotmail.co.uk
t: 07515419067

Multi-talented, Quick learner, Strives for
success, Skills in Adobe, CAD, 3D modelling,
maths/mechanics/FEA, Programming.

94 108

Network Directory
Es - Gu

Saba Eshraghi
Integrated Product Design MSc

e: saba_eshraghi@yahoo.com
t: 07575101394

 281

Stephanie Fox
Industrial Design & Technology BA

e: stephaniefox@tinyworld.co.uk
t: 07905183549

'In order to be irreplaceable, one must always be different'
Coco Chanel

 188 247

Manuel Esperon
Mechanical Engineering MSc

e: manuelesperon@hotmail.com
t: 07856951018

"We choose to go to the moon in this decade and do the other things, not because they are easy, but because they are hard" J.F. Kennedy

 176

Audley Franklin
Mech Eng with Building Services BEng

e: akfranklin@ntlworld.com
t: 07939171969

 174

Tom Etheridge
Industrial Design & Technology BA

e: tom@tometheridge.co.uk
w: www.tometheridge.co.uk
t: 07530869872

"People ignore design that ignores people'.
(Frank Chimero) This is my approach.

198 310

Luiza Frederico
Industrial Design BSc

e: luizabfrederico@hotmail.com
t: 07789261385

It is the role of the designer to facilitate the change of behaviours and values of the mass market in order for us to develop sustainably and responsibly.

22 165

Michael Evans
Product Design BSc

e: info@michael-evansdesign.com
w: www.michael-evansdesign.com
t: 07825956878

"One of the great things about books is sometimes there are some fantastic pictures."
- George W. Bush

80 109

Thomas Gale
Integrated Product Design MSc

e: tomyg10@hotmail.com
t: 07977577929

I believe a designer's job is to see what other people don't normally see. My work focuses on enhancing this ability in order to achieve success where others would not.

 275

Mia Foo
Product Design BSc

e: mail@miafoo.com
w: www.miafoo.com
t: 07840152691

I like to draw and make pretty things but the role of the designer is of utmost importance in keeping our planet healthy. I secretly wish I was a chocolatier.

 185

Colin Gallagher
Integrated Product Design MSc

e: gallaghercolin@hotmail.com
w: linkedin.com/in/colinjgallagher
t: 07952177874

I am an ambitious and creative designer building on my knowledge and understanding human psychology, and apply this to both product and system design.

41

362

Damariz Gárate Flores
Tecnológico de Monterrey, Campus Querétaro

e: damgaflo@gmail.com
w: http://www.qro.itesm.mx
t: +521(442)3187078

Nothing lasts forever so live it all, laugh it off, take chances, and never have regrets; because at one point everything you did is exactly what you wanted.

 339

Albany Gómez Limón
Tecnológico de Monterrey, Campus Querétaro

e: vitaminac.estudio@gmail.com
w: http://www.qro.itesm.mx
t: +(52) 442 1 13 41 34

The design is one of the most powerful tools to impact society, designers just need to involve diverse social groups in the developing process to make them part of the solution.

 336

Bhavin Gawali
Indian Institute of Technology Madras

e: bhavingawali@gmail.com
t: 91 9962364249

A practical thinker who believes in application of ideas. "An idea without application is a dead idea."

 342

Baboo Gowreesunker
Mech Eng with Building Services B. Eng

e: lesh_g@yahoo.com
t: 07789692840

104

Georgina Carmen Walther Silesky
Tecnológico de Monterrey, Campus Querétaro

e: georginawalther@hotmail.com
w: http://www.qro.itesm.mx
t: +521(442)1457545

The world can be a place full of beauty and opportunities; or a place where monsters hide. It's what you decide to do with what you've got.

 339

Neepun Goyal
Industrial Design & Technology BA

e: neepungoyal@hotmail.co.uk
t: 07912355922

I am a creative problem solver and an enthusiastic individual, my dedication to DESIGN is such, that what I do becomes a part of my life, and I enjoy it.

 239

Calliope Georgousi
Multimedia Technology & Design BSc

e: georgouk@gmail.com
w: www.calliopemuse.co.uk
t: 07564042023

My Multimedia Design skills vary from usability & design interaction to more technical ones, the likes of Adobe software and others.

292

Victoria Grantham
Industrial Design & Technology BA

e: granners_vicky@hotmail.co.uk
t: 07813442139

"Don't trip, don't stress"

 138 189

Amy Godsell
Industrial Design BSc

e: amygodsell@gmail.com
w: www.amygodsell.com
t: 07835604067

Amy is "a very accomplished graphic designer, great at communicating ideas & client liaison. Excellent professionalism & dedication, making her irreplaceable" O Morgan

 60   199

Mauricio Castaño Guiza
Design Strategy and Innovation MA

e: maurioc@gmail.com
t: 07760810880

Industrial designer with wide experience in creative and project management focused on furniture and exhibition design industries. Design Thinking applied to solve problems with different needs.

 267

James Gunton
Industrial Design & Technology BA

e: james.gunton@hotmail.co.uk
t: 07787446846

As an 'ideas' person University has taught me how to structure an initial idea, bring it to life then consider any potential for further development. I am naturally enthusiastic and have great energy and communicate well

 155  200

Andrew Heaton
Mechanical Engineering MSc

e: ae.h@live.co.uk
t: 07875164741

"Once you consent to some concession, you can never cancel it and put things back the way they are." - Howard Hughes

 176

Julia Hamid
Design Strategy & Innovation MA

e: joe@brunel.ac.uk
w: www.coroflot.com/julia_hamid
t: 07899835362

Proficient in 3D Cad; profound knowledge of design management & design research; develops innovation & branding strategies

 264

Karla Siu Hernández
Tecnológico de Monterrey, Campus Querétaro

e: karsiu@hotmail.com
w: http://www.qro.itesm.mx
t: (442) 2137713

Design is about making humans to get involved with their environment, to create wonderful feelings with everyday objects.

 340

Christopher Harkin
Industrial Design & Technology BA

e: Christopherharkin@hotmail.com
w: www.coroflot.com/ChrisHarkin
t: 07872045424

Finalist and Winner of the Highly Commended Award at the European Student Designer Lighting Awards 2008, EPRSC Bursary Winner 2009: Design for Dementia.

 190  246

Laura Hodge
Industrial Design & Technology BA

e: laurahodge@hotmail.co.uk
t: 07881717559

A creative, hard-working designer with a particular interest in Emotionally Durable Design and Product Form. "Create like a god, command like a king, work like a slave" – Brancusi

 61 74

Nick Harrod
Industrial Design & Technology BA

e: harrod.n@hotmail.co.uk
t: 07732669011

I have a great understanding and interest in Design for manufacture. I excel in the three dimensional modeling using CAD and love the buzz of producing final design solutions that work.

 201  309

Chris Holloway
Industrial Design BSc

e: mess@ukdesigners.org
w: www.mess.ukdesigners.org
t: 07853884696

A flexible and versatile designer, my style is functionally innovative, emphesising user centred factors, and aiming to improve the user's experience with a product.

 77  162

Andrew Haughton
Motorsport Engineering MEng

e: andyhaughton_15@hotmail.com
t: 07717725322

Over two years in Formula Student, I have designed a monocoque style Chassis for the 2010 Brunel Racing car and developed a Traction and Launch Control system.

 168

Bradly Hood
Industrial Design & Technology

e: info@ancientink.com
t: 07759222942

I am a very flexible designer with skills graphic, product and image design. Form and emotion are the basis to my design process.

 160  202

Samuel Isaac Delgado Durón

Tecnológico de Monterrey, Campus Querétaro

e: isakitou@gmail.com m
t: 52 449 1228597

To the optimists, the glass is half full, to
the pessimist the glass is half empty, to the
engineers, the glass is twice as it should be.

 337

Ziyi Jin

Integrated Product Design MSc

275

Luis Martínez Ambrosio Jakousi

Tecnológico de Monterrey, Campus Querétaro

e: mtza.luis@gmail.com
w: http://www.qro.itesm.mx
t: +52 (442) 2743048

Think. Do it. Succeed/Fail. Evolve

 340

Karl Jolly

Product Design Engineering BSc

e: karl@karljollydesign.co.uk
w: www.karljollydesign.co.uk
t: 07821556375

An enthusiastic, hard working and
efficient individual with a passion for
design.

191

Francisco Javier López Casique

Tecnológico de Monterrey, Campus Querétaro

e: javis887509@hotmail.com
w: http://www.qro.itesm.mx
t: +521(442)2042298

We just have one World, we need to take care
of it. If people forget that, we might show
some lights.

 339

Michael Jones

Industrial Design & Technology BA

e: michaeljljones@gmail.com
t: 07545217721

I make stuff... actually I make stuff up and
then try and do something with it... ironically
that's me.

 192 307

Saravanan Jeyendran

Product Design Engineering BSc

e: Savj5@hotmail.co.uk
t: 07888754218

Good with Pro e and minor electronics
knowledge.

95

Freddie Jordan

Industrial Design & Technology BA

e: Freddie_jordan6@hotmail.com
w: www.freddiejordandesign.com
t: 07972196122

Creative thinker inspired by innovative design.
"Any sufficiently advanced technology is
indistinguishable from magic" Arthur C Clarke

193 321

Luo Jianping

Tsinghua University

e: jianping1314zz@163.com
t: 86-010-62798872

I love fashion and I love design!

 331

José López Morales Servando

Tecnológico de Monterrey, Campus Querétaro

e: chepogg@hotmail.com
w: http://www.qro.itesm.mx
t: +52(442)2184387

Designing something new is easy, the
challenge lies on sustainable innovation,
while creating something new you ensure
public awareness will change.

 339

Network Directory
Jo - Le

Devraj Joshi
Product Design Engineering BSc

e: hello@go2dev.co.uk
w: www.go2dev.co.uk
t: 07900525624

Good design is not about pulling out all the stops; good design is knowing which stops to pull and how.

 98 110

Stephen Kago
Mechanical Engineering BEng

e: smwaura@yahoo.com
t: 07961953512

 172 172 174

Thelma Kalentzoti
Integrated Product Design MSc

e: thelkal@yahoo.com
t: 306978188202

Motivated by new social demands, I constantly seek innovation through design. Ethnographic research, packaging & product design inspire me to meet my aspirations for a better future.

 279

M. Yigit Karakilic
Simon Fraser University

e: yigitkarakilic@hotmail.com
w: www.inquedesign.com
t: 1-604-764-6263

"Push yourself again and again. Don't give an inch until the final buzzer sounds"

 334

Neerav Karani
Indian Institute of Technology Madras

e: niravkarani001@gmail.com
t: +91-9840677080

It's not what you look at that matters, it's what you see.

 343

Sharan Kaur
Industrial Design & Technology BA

e: Sharan_07@hotmail.co.uk
t: 07922935855

For myself the greater challenge is the ability to be attuned to the world around us, by emphasizing the human experience and interaction with products both mentally and physically.

 75  244

Alexia Kedra
Motorsport Engineering MEng

e: alexiakedra@msn.com
t: +30 6947308195

I have a good technique in drawing and painting and an indepth knowledge of most design software. I have also had a professional experience in setting up several exhibitions.

 256

Thomas Kelham
Industrial Design BSc

e: tom.kelham@hotmail.com
t: 07739986864

Don't use blue foam, use yellow its better!

 30 322

Anton Khmelev
Industrial Design & Technology BA

t: 07881717559

"We are all makers of our own future and have the power to influence the ones of others. As designers why not use this opportunity to make a change, enable and promote ones lives in a positive way."

212

Ohran Kim
Design Strategy & Innovation MA

e: orankim@naver.com
w: http://www.cyworld.com/oranaro
t: 07796890423

Based on architectural thinking I am crossing the boundary between theory and practice to realise design leadership for a socioculturally sustainable environment.

 268

Natalie King
Industrial Design BSc

e: nat.r.king@gmail.com
w: www.natalie-king.co.uk
t: 07821537337

Inspired by effective communication.
Placement with Chanel.
'Good design is obvious. Great design is
transparent.' Joe Sparano

 180  315

Tobi Lawal
Mechanical Engineering and Design MEng

e: Tobi.lawal@live.co.uk
w: www.tobilawal.co.uk
t: 07984554455

With a strong, unique engineering and design
background, I can innovative through design
in any context: Be that mechanical, service or
business strategy.

 194  308

Vasapol Kittipol
Industrial Design & Technology BA

e: Contact@vkittipol.com
w: www.vkittipol.com
t: 07912848749

I believe that product design must be as
simple as possible but not simpler; and
user-centred design should be at its heart.

 143

Martin Lawrence
Mechanical Engineering MEng

e: lawrence_martin@rocketmail.com
t: 07834864902

The glass is neither half full nor half empty, it
is twice the size it is required to be.

 176

Sanjeev Lal
Mechanical Engineering BEng

e: sanjeevlal_@hotmail.com
t: 07835594313

Engineering enthusiast, proficient in practical
innovative designs along with the ability to
model numerically and computationally to
high standards.

 69

Tom Le Mesurier
Industrial Design & Technology BA

e: tomlemesurier@hotmail.com
t: 07872968759

Creative thinker inspired and driven by seeing my
thoughts come to life, from sketches on a piece
of paper right through to a finished product.
Placement with SMP Playgrounds Ltd, design
engineer for playground equipment.

 62 101

Adam Lambert
Industrial Design & Technology BA

e: Adam_lambert@ntlworld.com
w: www.adamlambertdesign.co.uk
t: 07890039882

Innovative thinker with a keen interest in
embedded systems and problem solving.
Placement with Inscentinel Ltd.

97 117

Hyun Dong Lee
Integrated Product Design MSc

e: leedanny87@gmail.com
t: (852)6335-6208

Veteran of a 3 year Product Design and
Manufacture course, a mixture of product
design and manufacturing engineering, where
projects were generally based on DFM thinking.

280

Estefania Larracoechea González
Tecnológico de Monterrey, Campus Querétaro

e: estefania.larracoechea@hotmail.com
w: http://www.qro.itesm.mx
t: +52 (442) 2-16-48-50

Design equals passion. Passion rules one's life.

 341

Terrence Lee
Industrial Design BSc

e: terrencejlee@gmail.com
t: 07504300514
Proactive problem solver with a mind for
function and detail, placement with BAE
Systems
Good design goes to heaven; bad design goes
everywhere. -Mieke Gerritzen

 78 233

Norah Lewis
Industrial Design & Technology BA

e: Norahlewis@gmail.com
t: 07908029979

Throughout my degree I have continued to
develop my skills as a multi-disciplined designer
and have continuously made it my aim to
improve my skills in all fields surrounding
creative design and practical applications.

31   136

Tom Lewis
Industrial Design & Technology BA

e: tom@jmstuning.co.uk
w: www.jmstuning.co.uk
t: 07756147428

Modern engine tuning techniques should be
designed to speak the native electrical and
mechanical language of the subject vehicle,
not ignore & irreversibly damage it

99   163

James Littek
Broadcast Media Design & Technology BSc

e: esteightnine@hotmail.co.uk
t: 07983074389

293

Anthony Liu
Aerospace Engineering MEng

e: Anthony1iu1984@yahoo.couk
t: 07876563313

175

Ying Liu
Integrated Product Design MSc

e: ly-libra15@hotmail.com
t: 8613914755299

The well being of a person is characterized
by the quality of life they have. This is my
design aim.

280

Francis Lofthouse
Industrial Design BSc

e: francislofthouse@hotmail.com
t: 07717235626

My design focus primarily targets concept
generation and styling. Work placement – 12
months at PearsonLloyd.

130   195

Paola Lucie Loubli
Design and Brand Strategy MA

e: Paola.loubli@gmail.com
t: 07807549595

I have business talents in emotional - interactive
marketing, answering needs of creative space
development, a management of cultural
differences and a research for pure originality.

270

Chris Lynch
Industrial Design BSc

e: chrislynch@live.co.uk
w:
t: 07500773025

Experienced in ergonomic and
mechanical design and very dedicated.

63   103

Aleksandrs Malcevs
Industrial Design & Technology BA

e: info@alexandermaltseff.com
w: www.alexandermaltseff.com
t: 07961224405

I consider participating in made in Brunel
show as a great opportunity I hope that I will
be able to meet potential employers or people I
will be able to further co-operate with.

24   144

Leonard Marti
Integrated Product Design MSc

e: leonard.marti@bluewin.ch
w: uk.linkedin.com/in/leonardmarti
t: 07510318801

I am very interested in sustainability and
especially in finding ways to make the user
to be more responsible and more aware of its
impact on the environment.

277

Alejandro Berger
Tecnológico de Monterrey, Campus Querétaro

w: http://www.qro.itesm.mx
t: +52 (442) 1-18-64-42

Carpe diem

 341

Samantha Mire
Industrial Design BSc

e: samantha@samanthamire.co.uk
w: www. samanthamire.co.uk
t: 07980752979
Placement with Scott Wilson.
"Create your own visual style, let it be unique for yourself and yet identifiable for others"
- Orson Welles.

 70 112

Michael Matey
Industrial Design BSc

e: Michael. Matey@hotmail.co.uk
w: matmdesigns.com
t: 07852377400

Things have been designed for a reason, whether it's directed towards People or Nature. To design is to solve problems by identifying them and executing the best solutions.

 57 203

Kishan Mistry
Industrial Design BSc

e: kishanmistry@hotmail.com
w: www.kishdesign.co.uk
t: 07800602108

Studying at Brunel has been a challenge but all challenges have good outcomes and from my time here I have developed and broadened a range of design skills.

20 225

Peter McClelland
Industrial Design BSc

e: design@peterjm.co.uk
w: www.peterjm.co.uk
t: 07875200465

Open minded, London based, human centered, industrial designer. 'People ignore design that ignores people' Frank Chimero.

196 245

Mohit Mittal
Indian Institute of Technology Madras

e: mittal_emc@yahoo.com
t: 91-8056038014

"The secret to creativity is to know how to hide your sources" - Albert Einstein.

 342

Bruce McLavy
Simon Fraser University

e: brucemclavy@gmail.com
t: 778-686-1131

Life is discovery.

 334

Andrew Morley
Industrial Design BSc

e: andrewmorley@me.com
w: http://uk.linkedin.com/in/andrewjmorley
t: 07917106934

Design to me is exhilarating and fascinating. I strive to create design, which is inspiring, useful and inviting to others, encouraging people to think.

 150 286

Peter McQuillan
Aerospace Engineering MEng

e: peter.mcquillan@gmail.com
t: 07957218390

175

Toshiyuki Murata
Design & Branding Strategy MA

e: toshiyuki.m.p@gmail.com
t: 07540499211

The future of design needs to be more responsible and practical as well.

 263

Rob Musselbrook
Industrial Design & Technology BA

e: r.mussellbrook@live.com
t: 07779243825

Industrial Designer with a detailed understanding of the design process in theory and in application. An innovator with commercial awareness and attention to detail.

 81 🖥 323

Mitch Neofytou
Industrial Design BSc

e: mitchneo@live.com
t: 07545155125

Design can facilitate innovation and ideation applicable not only to product design but to any business involved in the creation of new value propositions.

◷ 21  126

John New
Integrated Product Design MSc

e: johnmnew@googlemail.com
t: 07882479336

I have a wide range of skills in the CS4 and CAD packages especially with Photoshop and Flash, also sketching and rendering. To me good design is simple.

 204 👥 235

Sahil Nurmohamed
Industrial Design BSc

e: sahilN@hotmail.co.uk
t: 07898107016

I always keep in mind the business aspect of design. Creating attractive and engaging products that work, are marketable and saleable and this is what good design is all about.

 240

Doreen Ojegba
Industrial Design BSc

e: doreen.ojegba@yahoo.com
t: 07958213394

I am a hardworking individual with a passion for design and a love for anything fresh and innovative.

◷ 28 ◷ 56

Gonzalo Pacheco Bravo
Tecnológico de Monterrey, Campus Querétaro

e: pachecogon@gmail.com
t: +52 (442) 3-77-72-01

Electronic Engineer who is willing to volunteer for any social project.

 341

Sergio Paul González Isidoro
Tecnológico de Monterrey, Campus Querétaro

e: mushurum@hotmail.com
t: +52(442)2383359

Dream, imagine, think, translate and create are the tools of a designer to change the world.

"Less is more" - Ludwig Mies van de Rohe

 337

César Paul Neria Hernández
Tecnológico de Monterrey, Campus Querétaro

e: cesarpaulnh@gmail.com
t: +52 442 500379

Think of you, think of the world, think of design.

 337

Lynne Peacock
Multimedia Technology & Design BSc

e: contact@lynnepeacock.com
w: www. lynnepeacock.com
t: 07950213910

Designer/developer motivated by pixels, web standards and usability.

🖥 290

Bo Peng
Integrated Product Design MSc

e: doctorpb1985@hotmail.com
t: 07835379391

🖥 281

Matthew Perry
Product Design BSc

e: mjp@matthewperrydesign.co.uk
w: www.matthewperrydesign.co.uk/
t: 07875259314

Professional, Passionate and Dedicated.

 82  113

Theresa Pert
Multimedia Technology & Design BSc

e: tpert@secremedia.com
w: www.secremedia.com
t: 08452939351

Freelance Multimedia Consultant providing
solutions for SMEs and London-based
Universities through 'Secremedia'.

 291

Nicholas Pettett
Industrial Design & Technology BA

e: nickpettett@gmail.com
t: 07921385784

Practical thinker inspired by creative problem
solving. Placement with Precision Lighting
Ltd. "There is no design without discipline.
There is no discipline without intelligence."
- Massimo Vignelli.

 64 197

Tom Pilgrim
Product Design BSc

e: design@tompilgrim.co.uk
w: www.tompilgrim.co.uk
t: 07904609136

I am a practical person interested in the
functional side of design. I really enjoy model
making either in 3D or in real life.

 114  205

Leonardo Pinho
Design & Branding Strategy MA

e: leo.pinho@gmail.com
t: 07858394637

Design management and creative thinking to
establish a powerful communication between
brands and people.

 265

Chris Place
Industrial Design & Technology BA

e: c.place@live.com
t: 07912317277

An internship at Tangerine and working
with GST during my major project have
given me a wealth of practical experience in
Industrial and Medical Design.

 84 128

Diego Rafael Torres Lafuente
Tecnológico de Monterrey, Campus Querétaro

e: diegortl@hotmail.com
t: +52 (442) 2383359

Technology must be created and used for
human and environmental benefits, not for
one's convenience.

 336

Hem Rampal
Indian Institute of Technology Madras

e: hemrampal@gmail.com
t: 91 9444546571

An intuitive and creative thinker who loves to solve
problems. Up to date with the latest technological
developments, he believes in applying them
whenever and wherever possible.

 104

Francisco Rebello
Industrial Design & Technology BA

e: franciscorebello@hotmail.co.uk
w: www.franciscorebello.com
t: 07789726505

An open-minded concept generator, communicator
and creative with strong graphic design ability.
12 month placement experience in graphic design
at Disney Interactive Studios.

 206

Christopher Richmond
Industrial Design & Technology BA

e: Chris@chrisandrobert.co.uk
w: www.chrisandrobert.co.uk
t: 07525365233

Innovative design thinker, with industry
experience with Wolff Olins, CTM-design and
Camouflage.

32

Alex Rincon
Product Design Engineering BSc

e: alex100587@gmail.com
w: www.ard-design.com
t: 07779243825

I began this course thinking design was just about sketching and making, but over the years I learnt that the opportunities were endless.

 115

Freddie Ryder
Product Design Engineering BSc

e: freddieryder@me.com
t: 07766564019

I always keep in mind the business aspect of design. Creating attractive and engaging products that work are marketable and saleable and is what good design is all about.

 214

Heather Roberts
Multimedia Technology & Design BSc

e: heatherroberts@live.com
w: www.heatherroberts.co.uk
t: 07976048897

My main interests in multimedia lie in creating interactive projects; I really enjoy the challenge of combining the skills needed in coding with those required for design.

 296

Shikha Sabharwal
Design Strategy & Innovation MA

e: shikhadesigns@gmail.com
w: http://uk.linkedin.com/in/sshikha
t: 07872492272

My passion is using design thinking as a tool, to transform individual experiences into powerful solutions for both businesses & communities

 272

Begoña Rodríguez Mondragón
Tecnológico de Monterrey, Campus Querétaro

e: begociraptor@gmail.com
t: +52 442 2143162

I'm a software engineer in the shape of a woman. Perfection is what guides me, passion is what drives me.

 337

Israel Salas Velasco
Tecnológico de Monterrey, Campus Querétaro

e: cw3688@hotmail.com
t: +52 (442) 1896895

Think about small steps and you will be able to walk longer roads.

 339

Eleanor Rogers
Product Design Engineering BSc

e: Eleanor.rogers42@googlemail.com
w: www.elerogers.co.uk
t: 07982723551

Interested in how empathy can improve design in Medical and Inclusive fields.

 116 216

Nick Salpingidis
Product Design BSc

e: nicksalpingidis@gmail.com
t: 07546456931

During the three years course in Product Design and several part time placements, I have gained experience. This has increased my levels of creativity and inspiration.

 142

Theodore Rutter
Mechanical Engineering MEng

e: Trutter123@msn.com
t: 07789310870

I have a keen interest in all forms of motorsport but particularly prototype motorcycle racing.

 079

Gabriel Salvador Tejeda
Tecnológico de Monterrey, Campus Querétaro

e: gabrielux88@hotmail.com
t: +52 (442)1465882

Generating social awareness in the quantities of alcohol ingested by person is a very relevant issue nowadays, as hundreds of people keep getting killed by the use of this drug.

 340

Louisa Santilli
Industrial Design & Technology BA

e: Louisa@santilli.me.uk
t: 07852501992

With all things in life I keep in mind William Morris' words: 'Have nothing in your houses that you do not know to be useful, or believe to be beautiful.'

 83 149

Jaymes Schular
Industrial Design & Technology BA

e: jschular@hotmail.co.uk
t: 07954340461

I like to use a combination of drawing skills, model making and 3D CAD in my design work.

 207 229

Arda Sesli
Design & Branding Strategy MA

e: ardasesli@yahoo.com.tr
t: 0 7766915329

My expertise mainly focus on industrial design, design management, branding and design strategies.

 257

Shruti Shah
Integrated Product Design MSc

278

Vishal Shah
Mech Eng with Building Services Beng

e: kipper70@hotmail.com
t: 07951226681

 174

Minyan Shao
Integrated Product Design MSc

e: sara_lexy8610@126.com
t: 07540196863

275

Daniel Sheard
Motorsport Engineering MEng

e: danjsheard@googlemail.com
t: 07763977397

"if you cant fix it with a hammer, you have an electrical problem"

 168

Srinath Sibi
Indian Institute of Technology Madras

e: sibisrinath@gmail.com
t: 91-9940219620

"If a man does his best, what else is there?" - General George S. Patton

343

Gilbert Sinnott
Multimedia Technology & Design BSc

e: gilbert.sinnott@gmail.com
w: gsinnott.kaen.org
t: 07789726505

"The computer can't tell you the emotional story. It can give you the exact mathematical design, but what's missing is the eyebrows." - Frank Zappa

297

Simon Smith
Industrial Design BSc

e: simonsmith1988@gmail.com
w: www.scdesign.co.uk
t: 07502206962

12 months in San Francisco has taught . We must be inclusive, considerate, and mindful of the future. Only in doing this can we truly meet the demands of an ever-changing world.

 209 314

Joe Snowdon
Industrial Design BSc

e: joesnowdonphoto@gmail.com
t: 07984058954

An individual with experience in many aspects of design. Well travelled.

 39   241

Terry Stokes
Industrial Design BSc

e: terrencejamesstokes@hotmail.com
t: 07957413275

Good design should always be an equal mix of science, art, passion and most of all hard work with the upmost attention to detail.

 211   211 220

Daniel Sparrow
Industrial Design & Technology BA

e: d-sparrow@live.com
w: www.dansparrow.co.uk
t: 07731318373

I love getting stuck into projects, especialy the hands on parts. I have a good sense of what does and doesn't work, and enjoy seeing products through from concept to creation.

 104

Sabrina Tan
Integrated Product Design MSc

e: sabrinawtan@gmail.com
t: 1-650-302-6203

Passionate about design that makes a difference in people's life. My designs are inspired by how people interact with their environment.

 274

Annabelle Spender
Industrial Design & Technology BA

e: aspender@lillyringlet.eu
w: www.lillyringlet.eu
t: 07965605999

Experienced in disability design, long term rebranding, photography, human centred design, CAD design and management on live projects

210   234

Jestine Philipose Thomas
Aerospace Engineering MSc

e: jestwils@gmail.com
t: 07551327231

 176

Viviana Stecconi
Design & Branding Strategy MA

e: vivianastecconi@gmail.com
t: 07846703145

Design thinking is my philosophy of life. Observation and curiosity are my key attitude that help you to follow innovation and trend and interest keep me alive.

258

Jithin Thomas
Aerospace Engineering MSc

e: jithinthomas86@gmail.com
t: 07762919695

"I am an Engineer, I serve mankind, by making dreams come true..." - Anon

176

James Stephens
Motorsport Engineering MEng

t: 07909731451

 168

Anil Toora
Industrial Design & Technology BA

e: aniltoora@hotmail.com
w: www.aniltoora.com
t: 07747772522

As a designer I enjoy designing products which have the potential to be realised in today's day and age with attention to detail playing a major role in my design process.

213

Thanh Tran
Product Design BSc

e: info@tantran.co.uk
w: www.tantran.co.uk
t: 07717534487

Energetic and enthusiastic design engineer with
extensive experience in engineering and design
across many disciplines.

 34

Jon Walmsley
Industrial Design BSc

e: Walmsley.jon@googlemail.com
t: 07988659621

Passionate about Eco Design, pushing for a
new generation of Design Philanthropy.

 87   127

Daniel Trigg
Industrial Design BSc

e: DanielPaulTrigg@hotmail.com
t: 07886250828

Design is not just about aesthetics, its about
creating a solution to a problem in the most user
friendly way.

Placements with Topshop/Topman Graphic Design.

 86   🖥 316

Patrick Walton
Aerospace Engineering MEng with MPDS

e: pwalton134@hotmail.com

Working with the team on BHL-06 has
given me a greater understanding of
exactly what it takes to design an aircraft
from scratch, within the constraints of the
specification.

 175

Ana Varenka De la Vega Díaz
Tecnológico de Monterrey, Campus Querétaro

e: varenka.di@gmail.com
t: +52 (442) 1106905

When you see something that wakes your feelings
it means a designer is behind it.

🔗 338

Ding Wang
Integrated Product Design MSc

e: koenmading@hotmail.com
t: +86 (138) 11880698

Multi-perspective thinking benefited from
Integrated Product Design.Comprehensive
creation stimulated by daily life.

👥 280

Marianne Waite
MA Design & Branding Strategy

e: mcwdesign@hotmail.co.uk
w: www.mariannewaite.co.uk
t: 07849083023

Experienced Digital Artist, Fine Artist and
Graphic Designer with a love for Branding
and Star Wars.

👥 226

Yanjiao Wang
Integrated Product Design MSc

e: wangyanjiao-003@163.com
t: 07832326606

👥 281

Thomas Wakeling
Product Design BSc

e: contact@dorisfilms.com
w: www.dorisfilms.com/tomwakeling.html
t: 07872966367

"Get to the chopper!" - Arnold Schwarzenegger

 35    139

Simon Warne
Industrial Design & Technology BA

e: Simon-Warne@hotmail.co.uk
t: 07813759273

An innovative and creative design thinker,
with 5 years previous experience working
within the fields of furniture and interior
design.

 88   135

Network Directory
Wi - Zh

Tom Williams
Industrial Design BSc

e: tom.williamsj13@gmail.com
t: 07894266701

Brunel Design has been a fantastic and challenging experience, and I'm so glad I didn't succumb to the temptation of going back to Dorset to sell ice creams.

36   221

Qianjun Wu
Tsinghua University

e: awu1211@yahoo.com.cn
t: 86 13581846408

Beijing based designer, committed to digging user value while focus on creative user research.

332

Luke Wilson
Industrial Design BSc

e: Ljwilson1111@hotmail.com
t: 07540749839

In 12 months of working and living in China I gained invaluable practical design and life experience to accompany the broad set of abilities fine-tuned at Brunel

68   317

Hugh Wyeth
Multimedia Technology & Design BSc

e: hughwyeth@gmail.com
w: www.hughwyeth.com
t: 07814895088

I'm a 3D artist specialising in modelling. I've completed a year's placement as a 3D artist at Mediatonic and hope to become a professional 3D artist.

288   294

Elizabeth Wolesley-Hext
Product Design Engineering BSc

e: elizabethhext@hotmail.co.uk
t: 07962068367

God did not create us to count days but to make days count.

89

Xingnuo Chen
Tsinghua University

e: cxn_30.student@sina.com
t: +00 (861) 3520606005

333

Joe-Simon Wood
Industrial Design & Technology BA

e: joesimon.wood@googlemail.co.uk
t: 0790734359

"A common mistake that people make when trying to design something completely foolproof is to underestimate the ingenuity of complete fools."- Douglas Adams

37   224

Frankie Yan
Simon Fraser University

e: frankie.lk.yan@gmail.com
t: 1-604-721-5714

As an ever-learning student of design, I strive to distant my work from uniformity, to create something out of the ordinary, and instil a cupful of innovation.

334

Oliver Wooderson
Design Strategy & Innovation MA

e: mail@oliverwooderson.com
w: www.oliverwooderson.com
t: 07739308280

Design is a powerful strategic tool. Harnessing creative thinking enables the exploration of complex problems and the creation of cutting edge innovations.

269

Richard Young
Integrated Product Design MSC

e: rich.young@live.com
t: 07745486716

I feel confident in my abilities, both as a designer and a strategist, and look forward to working within a challenging design environment.

279

Fu Yu
Tsinghua University

e: yutouhappy@163.com
t: +00 (861) 5901317254

A very curious explorer interested in psychology and philosophy. 1st year student in industrial design with a background of Automotive Body Engineering.

 328

Paul Yuan
Simon Fraser University

e: pyuana@gmail.com
w: www.paulyuan.ca
t: 1-778-554-7976

I aspire to tackle meaningful problems and create solutions that make a difference.

 334

Minying Zhu
Integrated Product Design MSC

e: summa1986@hotmail.com
t: 07865986987

I always wanted to be a designer and since I've come to the UK I have really started to feel that design can change the world. Even if it is just tiny everyday things.

 274

Notes:

Notes:

MADE IN BRUNEL™
Innovation that works